KS3
Success

Workbook

Science
SATs
Levels 3-6

Brian Arnold • Hannah Kingston • Emma Poole

Contents

Biology

Chemistry

Physics

Homework diary

TOPIC	STUDY DATE	SCORE
Life processes and cells		/27
Organ systems		/26
Nutrition and food tests		/27
The digestive system		/26
The heart		/23
Blood and circulation		/27
Movement		/30
The lungs and breathing		/26
The menstrual cycle		/24
Reproduction		/21
Drugs		/23
Fighting disease		/25
Photosynthesis		/25
Plant reproduction		/30
Carbon and nitrogen cycles		/25
Classification		/21
Variation		/27
Food chains and webs		/22
Adaptation		/21
Rocks		/22
The rock cycle		/24
Pollution		/18
States of matter		/27
Dissolving		/18
Particle theory		/20
Atoms and elements		/23
Metals		/34
Unusual elements		/16
Chemical reactions		/26
Reactivity series		/21
Displacement		/30
Acids and alkalis		/31
Making salts		/26
Chemical tests		/26
Mixtures		/34
Separation techniques		/21
Compounds		/28
Naming compounds		/26
Symbols		/30
Speed		/33
Graphs of motion		/23
Forces		/24
Friction and terminal velocity		/29
Moments		/27
Pressure		/28
Light rays and reflection		/29
Refraction and colour		/24
Sounds		/34
Echoes and hearing		/29
Energy		/31
Using energy resources		/35
Alternative sources of energy		/26
Heat transfer		/29
Circuits and components		/33
Circuits: current and voltage		/20
Magnets and electromagnets		/36
The Earth in space		/28

Progress plotter

Once you have completed a unit, and filled in your score on the Homework Diary opposite, use this Progress Plotter to chart your success! Fill in the boxes with your score for each unit and watch your results get better and better.

	Nearly all right – **Excellent work!**	*More than half –* **Good – but keep trying.**	*Less than half –* **Room for improvement.**	*Under 5 –* **Needs more work.**
Life processes and cells				
Organ systems				
Nutrition and food tests				
The digestive system				
The heart				
Blood and circulation				
Movement				
The lungs and breathing				
The menstrual cycle				
Reproduction				
Drugs				
Fighting disease				
Photosynthesis				
Plant reproduction				
Carbon and nitrogen cycles				
Classification				
Variation				
Food chains and webs				
Adaptation				
Rocks				
The rock cycle				
Pollution				
States of matter				
Dissolving				
Particle theory				
Atoms and elements				
Metals				
Unusual elements				
Chemical reactions				
Reactivity series				
Displacement				
Acids and alkalis				
Making salts				
Chemical tests				
Mixtures				
Separation techniques				
Compounds				
Naming compounds				
Symbols				
Speed				
Graphs of motion				
Forces				
Friction and terminal velocity				
Moments				
Pressure				
Light rays and reflection				
Refraction and colour				
Sounds				
Echoes and hearing				
Energy				
Using energy resources				
Alternative sources of energy				
Heat transfer				
Circuits and components				
Circuits: currents and voltage				
Magnets and electromagnets				
The Earth in space				

Life processes and cells

Cells are the building blocks of life. All living things are made up of cells. A living thing is called an organism. Plants and animals are organisms.

A Choose just one answer, a, b, c or d.

1 What does a plant cell have that an animal cell does not? (1 mark)
a) nucleus   b) chloroplast
c) cell membrane   d) cytoplasm

2 What is a specialised cell? (1 mark)
a) a cell that has changed its shape to do a particular job
b) a cell with an unusual shape
c) a group of cells working together
d) a cell that only has one job

3 Which of these is not a process of living things?
a) movement   b) reproduction
c) respiration   d) talking   (1 mark)

4 Which part of the cell contains genetic information? (1 mark)
a) cytoplasm
b) vacuole
c) nucleus
d) cell wall

5 What is an organ? (1 mark)
a) a group of cells
b) a mammal
c) a group of organs
d) a group of tissues working together

Score   /5

B Answer all parts of all questions.

1 Match up these activities to these life processes. (7 marks)

Movement	Getting rid of waste
Excretion	Releasing energy from food
Reproduction	Eating
Growth	Escaping from danger
Sensitivity	Producing offspring
Nutrition	Reaching adult size
Respiration	Reacting to changes

2 Fill in the missing words to show the similarities and differences between an animal and plant cell. (4 marks)

Animal and plant cells both have a nucleus, ..., and ....

Only plant cells have a vacuole, ... and ....

3 Name two specialised animal cells and one specialised plant cell. (3 marks)

....

....

Score   /14

C This is a SATs-style question. Answer all parts of the question.

1 The diagram below shows some specialised cells. They each have different functions.

A

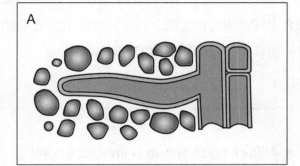

B

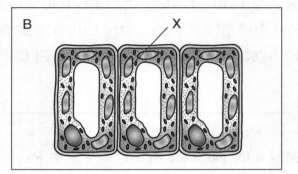

C

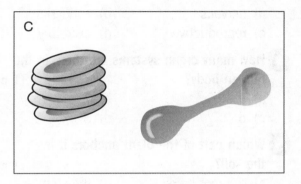

D

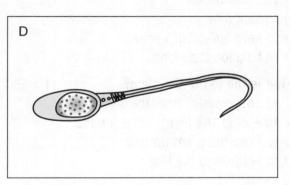

a) The main functions of the four cells are listed below. Write the letter of the cell next to its function. (4 marks)

(i)   carries oxygen ....

(ii) photosynthesis ....

(iii) absorbs water from the soil ....

(iv) fertilise an egg ....

b) Name the part labelled X on cell B. (1 mark)

....

c) What is the function of the part labelled X? (1 mark)

....

d) Why does cell A not have the part labelled X? (1 mark)

....

e) Give the name of the part of the body where cell D is produced. (1 mark)

....

Score   /8

How well did you do?   1–7 Try again   8–12 Getting there   13–19 Good work   20–27 Excellent!

For more help on this topic see KS3 Science Success Guide pages 4–5

Organ systems

Plants can be divided up into five main parts. The five parts work together so that the plant can carry out the seven life processes. Humans have nine organ systems that enable them to carry out the life processes.

A Choose just one answer, a, b, c or d.

1 What is the job of the leaf? (1 mark)
  a) photosynthesis
  b) to look nice
  c) to keep the plant upright
  d) to balance the plant

2 What is the job of the stem? (1 mark)
  a) to obtain water from the soil
  b) to anchor the plant in the ground
  c) to keep the plant upright
  d) to hold on to the leaf

3 Which organ system is involved in getting rid of waste? (1 mark)
  a) nervous   b) endocrine
  c) reproductive   d) excretory

4 How many organ systems are there in the human body? (1 mark)
  a) 9   b) 7
  c) 6   d) 3

5 Which part of the plant anchors it in the soil? (1 mark)
  a) the root hairs   b) the stem
  c) the root   d) the flower

Score /5

B Answer all parts of all questions.

1 Unscramble the letters to reveal the 9 organ systems of the human body. (9 marks)

lketsale   s..............   lcsmue   m..............

orrsptyeiar   r..............   gtvidseei   d..............

yorcuirclat   c..............   dtvierpreouc r..............

svnreuo   n..............   orexrtcey   e..............

cnirednoe   e..............

2 Label this diagram of a flowering plant. (4 marks)

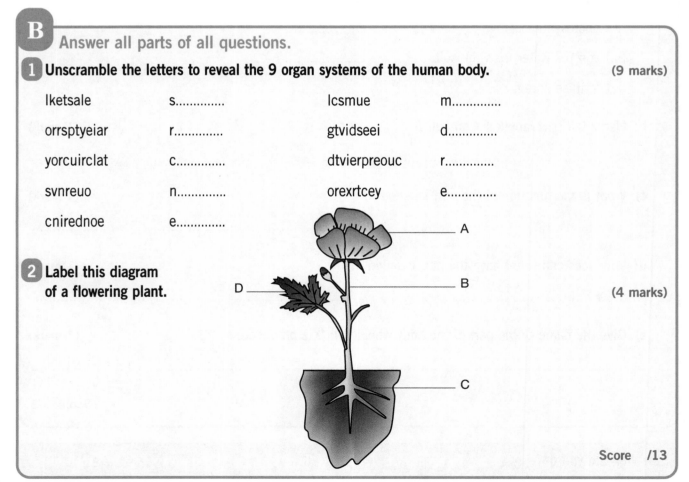

Score /13

8

C This is a SATs-style question. Answer all parts of the question.

1 The diagram below shows the main organs of the human excretory system

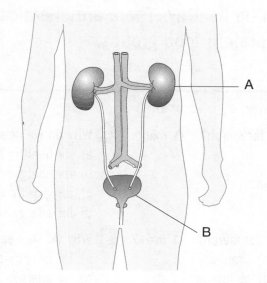

A

B

a) Label the organs of the human excretory system.   (2 marks)

A ....

B ....

b) What is the function of part B?   (1 mark)

....

c) Name the organ system that uses our sense organs to detect changes in the
environment.   (1 mark)

....

d) Each organ system has a different function. Write the name of the organ system next to its
function.   (4 marks)

Function	Name of system
support, protection and movement	....
digesting food	....
transporting blood around the body	....
breathing and gas exchange	....

Score   /8

How well did you do?   1–7 Try again   8–12 Getting there   13–19 Good work   20–26 Excellent!

For more help on this topic see KS3 Science Success Guide pages 6–7

9

Nutrition and food tests

A balanced diet consists of 7 food groups. These provide all the nutrients that the body needs to be healthy. There are chemical tests for the carbohydrate, fat and protein food groups.

A Choose just one answer, a, b, c or d.

1 What is the chemical test for starch? (1 mark)
a) Benedict's solution
b) iodine solution
c) water
d) Biuret test

2 What is the positive result for starch? (1 mark)
a) purple   b) orange
c) blue/black   d) yellow

3 What is the chemical test for glucose? (1 mark)
a) Benedict's solution and heat
b) Biuret test
c) iodine solution
d) just Benedict's

4 Why do we need glucose in our diet? (1 mark)
a) for healthy bones and teeth
b) for energy
c) for growth and repair
d) for energy storage

5 Why do we need protein in our diet? (1 mark)
a) for healthy bones and teeth
b) for energy
c) for growth and repair
d) for energy storage

Score   /5

B Answer all parts of all questions.

1 Draw lines to match up the food group with its function in the body. (6 marks)

Food group	Function
proteins	needed in small amounts to keep healthy
carbohydrates	store of energy and insulation
fibre	for immediate energy
water	growth and repair of cells
fats	keeps food moving through the gut
vitamins and minerals	allows chemical reactions to take place

2 Use words from the list to fill in the gaps. (8 marks)

Biuret   Benedict's   iodine   blue/black   purple   orange   ethanol   cloudy white

To test a food solution to see if it contained sugar we would use the .... test and heat it.
The colour of the solution would turn .... if sugar is present. To test for starch we would use
.... The colour would be .... if starch were present. To test for fat .... would be used.
A positive result would mean the solution turning .... Finally, the test for protein is the
.... test. The solution would turn .... if protein were present.

Score   /14

C This is a SATs-style question. Answer all parts of the question.

1 The label below is from a jar of pasta sauce.

Nutritional information

Average values per 100g   Ingredients

Energy   791 kilojoule   Tomatoes, Onions, Cheese, Sugar,

Protein   2.0 g   Double Cream, Garlic, Flavourings,

Carbohydrate 4.9 g   Spices, Herbs.

Fat   18.2 g

a) Which two types of nutrient supply us with most of our energy needs?   (2 marks)

....

....

b) Give the name of one nutrient that is missing from the list.   (1 mark)

....

c) Which item in the list of ingredients has the most protein per gram?   (1 mark)

....

d) Give two reasons why we need protein in our diets.   (2 marks)

....

....

e) How could we test the pasta sauce to see if it contained any starch?   (2 marks)

....

....

Score   /8

How well did you do?   1–7 Try again   8–12 Getting there   13–19 Good work   20–27 Excellent!

The digestive system

- The digestive system is really one long tube called the gut. If it were unravelled it would be about nine metres long.
- Digestion begins with the mouth and ends at the anus.
- Food normally takes food 24–28 hours to pass through your digestive system.

A Choose just one answer, a, b, c or d.

1 Where does digestion begin? **(1 mark)**
a) stomach   b) mouth
c) small intestine d) rectum

2 Where is digestion completed? **(1 mark)**
a) small intestine b) large intestine
c) stomach   d) liver

3 What do proteins get broken down into? **(1 mark)**
a) amino acids   b) glucose
c) starch   d) fatty acids

4 What does starch get broken down into? **(1 mark)**
a) amino acids
c) glucose   d) glycerol

5 What do large insoluble molecules get broken down into? **(1 mark)**
a) large soluble molecules
b) small soluble molecules
c) medium soluble molecules
d) small insoluble molecules

Score /5

B Answer all parts of all questions.

1 The three main enzymes in the digestive system are lipases, carbohydrases and proteases. Which of them digests: **(3 marks)**

a) protein   ....
b) fats   ....
c) carbohydrates?   ....

2 What are these food types digested into? **(3 marks)**

a) protein   ....
b) fats   ....
c) carbohydrates?   ....

3 Which of the following parts of the digestive system are the odd ones out? **(3 marks)**

stomach   gall bladder   small intestine   pancreas   liver   oesophagus

....

4 Name the 4 types of teeth. **(4 marks)**

....
....

Score /13

C This is a SATs-style question. Answer all parts of the question.

1 The diagram shows the organs of the digestive system.

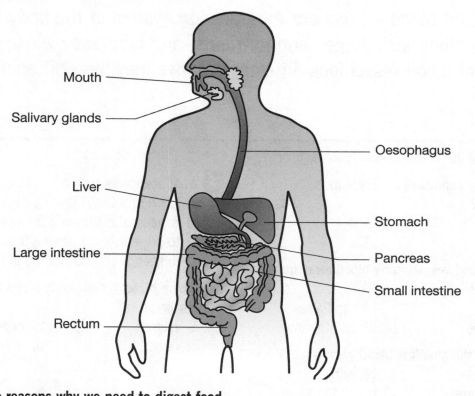

Mouth

Salivary glands

Liver

Large intestine

Rectum

Oesophagus

Stomach

Pancreas

Small intestine

a) Give two reasons why we need to digest food. (2 marks)

....

....

b) Where in the digestive system is digestion completed? (1 mark)

....

c) What is the name of the chemicals that help us digest our food? (1 mark)

....

d) Match the organ of the digestive system with its function (4 marks)

Function

• removes excess water and salt from undigested food

• adds saliva and mixes up food

• produces bile

• secretes gastric juices and churns up the food

Organ

• stomach

• mouth

• large intestine

• liver

Score   /8

The heart

The heart and blood vessels are the transport system of the body. They provide the body with oxygen and nutrients, and take away waste products. The types of blood vessel look different because they have different functions.

A Choose just one answer, a, b, c or d.

1 How many chambers are there in the heart? **(1 mark)**
a) 3
b) 4
c) 2
d) 1

2 Which blood vessels carry blood away from the heart? **(1 mark)**
a) veins
b) capillaries
c) arteries
d) all of them

3 What are the smallest blood vessels? **(1 mark)**
a) arteries
b) veins
c) capillaries
d) all the same

4 What are valves for? **(1 mark)**
a) to prevent blood flowing backwards
b) to keep blood flowing backwards
c) to prevent blood flowing to some areas
d) to keep the blood flowing at high pressure

5 Which blood vessels carry blood at low pressure? **(1 mark)**
a) arteries
b) capillaries
c) veins
d) only the vena cava

Score /5

B Answer all parts of all questions.

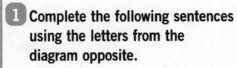

1 Complete the following sentences using the letters from the diagram opposite. **(6 marks)**

.... is the blood vessel that goes to the lungs to collect oxygen.

.... is the main artery that takes blood to the body.

.... is the part of the heart that receives blood from the lungs.

.... is the main vein that brings back blood from the body.

.... is the blood vessel that comes back from the lungs.

.... is the part of the heart with the thickest walls.

2 What does oxygenated blood mean? **(1 mark)**

....

B (Continued)

3 What does deoxygenated blood mean? (1 mark)

....

4 Which side of the heart contains oxygenated blood? (1 mark)

....

5 Which side of the heart contains deoxygenated blood? (1 mark)

....

Score /10

C

This is a SATs-style question. Answer all parts of the question.

1 The diagram shows the three blood vessels in the body.

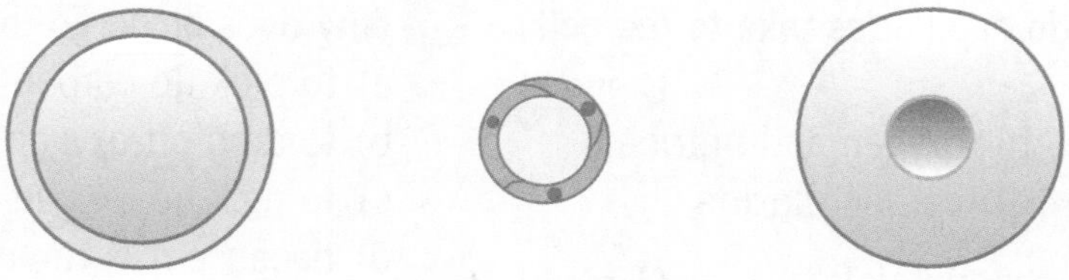

A   B   C

a) Which of the blood vessels is the (3 marks)
   (i)   artery?   ....
   (ii) vein?   ....
   (iii) capillary?   ....

b) How could you tell which of the three blood vessels was the capillary? (1 mark)

....

c) What do veins have that prevent blood flowing backwards? (1 mark)

....

d) Which organ of the body provides the force to pump blood around the body? (1 mark)

....

e) Sally wanted to measure her pulse rate. Which kind of blood vessel would she feel in her wrist or neck? (1 mark)

....

f) When would her pulse rate be the highest: before or after exercise? (1 mark)

....

Score /8

How well did you do?   1–4 Try again   5–9 Getting there   10–16 Good work   17–23 Excellent!

Blood and circulation

Blood flows around the body in blood vessels. The heart provides the force needed for this. The path taken around the body is called the circulatory system and it follows a specific route. Blood consists of four parts, each with its own job in the body.

A Choose just one answer, a, b, c or d.

1 What is the job of the red blood cells?
   a) to carry oxygen   (1 mark)
   b) defence against disease
   c) to clot blood
   d) to transport dissolved substances

2 What substances do capillaries take to the cells of the body?   (1 mark)
   a) oxygen only   b) oxygen and nutrients
   c) nutrients only   d) carbon dioxide

3 What is the job of the platelets?   (1 mark)
   a) defence against disease
   b) to clot blood
   c) to carry oxygen
   d) to carry hormones

4 What is the role of white blood cells?
   a) to clot blood   (1 mark)
   b) to carry oxygen
   c) to carry nutrients
   d) defence against disease

5 Why does blood go to the lungs?   (1 mark)
   a) to pick up carbon dioxide
   b) to drop off oxygen
   c) to pick up oxygen
   d) because it is the closest organ

Score   /5

B Answer all parts of all questions.

1 Fill in the gaps.   (9 marks)

Blood is made up of four main parts. They are the ...., ..., ... and plasma.

The plasma is a watery liquid that contains soluble food, salts, and ....

The .... carry oxygen around the body and the .... fight infection and disease.
The .... clot blood if you cut yourself.

The blood follows a specific route around the body. The .... provides the force to pump the blood around.

2 What does the blood deliver to the cells of the body?   (1 mark)

....

3 What does blood take away from the cells of the body?   (1 mark)

....

4 Match the label to the correct diagram.

white blood cell ....   (3 marks)

red blood cell ....

platelet ....

Score   /14

C This is a SATs-style question. Answer all parts of the question.

1 The list shows the 4 parts of blood. Use the words to answer the questions that follow.

white blood cells   red blood cells   platelets   plasma

a) Nisha had a cold. Which blood cell would help her fight her cold?   (1 mark)

   ....

b) Which type of blood cell carries oxygen around the body?   (1 mark)

   ....

c) Which part of the blood helps clot the blood if you cut yourself?   (1 mark)

   ....

The following list shows some substances carried around the body in the plasma

carbon dioxide   glucose   vitamins   urea

d) Which two of these substances are waste products produced by the body?   (2 marks)

   ....

   ....

The diagram below shows a red blood cell and a white blood cell.

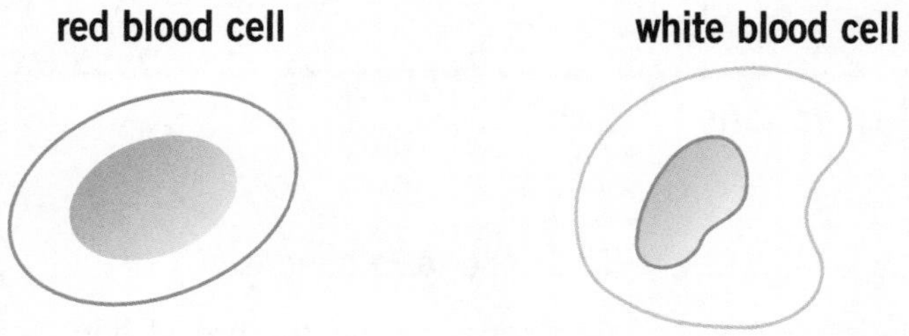

red blood cell   white blood cell

e) Apart from their function, what is the other difference between these two cells?   (1 mark)

   ....

f) What other important features do red blood cells have that help them carry oxygen to all
   parts of the body?   (2 marks)

   ....

   ....

Score   /8

How well did you do?   1–7 Try again   8–12 Getting there   13–19 Good work   20–27 Excellent!

Movement

The human body is able to move because of the skeleton, muscles and joints. The central nervous system controls this movement with the use of sense organs.

A Choose just one answer, a, b, c or d.

1 Ligaments attach: (1 mark)
a) muscle to bone
b) bone to bone
c) tendons to muscle
d) muscle to muscle

2 Tendons attach: (1 mark)
a) bone to bone
b) muscle to bone
c) tendons to muscle
d) muscle to muscle

3 Muscles can only: (1 mark)
a) push   b) push and pull
c) not move   d) pull

4 What is the function of cartilage? (1 mark)
a) It is a muscle.
b) It is a tendon.
c) It acts as a shock absorber.
d) It is a ligament.

5 How many types of sense organ do we have? (1 mark)
a) 4   b) 5
c) 6   d) 2

Score   /5

B Answer all parts of all questions.

1 Complete the following. (4 marks)

The longest bone in the body is .... The upper arm bone is ....

Another name for the patella is .... Another name for the breast bone is ....

2 State whether the following are true or false. (6 marks)

The knee joint is an example of a ball and socket joint. ....

The synovial fluid acts as a shock absorber. ....

Cartilage is at the end of bones. ....

Muscles can only pull not push. ....

Muscles are attached to bones by tendons. ....

Bones are held together by tendons. ....

3 Our five sense organs detect changes in the environment. To what do our sense organs respond? (5 marks)

eyes ....   nose ....

ears ....   tongue ....

skin ....

Score   /15

C This is a SATs-style question. Answer all parts of the question.

1 The diagram below shows the joints and muscles in the arm.

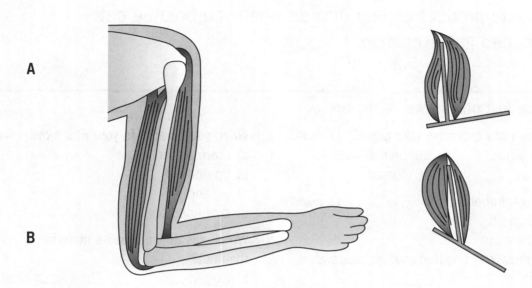

A

B

a) On the diagram above draw a line from the letter A to a muscle and a line from the letter B to a tendon. (2 marks)

....

b) What is the job of the tendons? (1 mark)

....

c) The elbow joint is a hinge joint. Name:

(i) a ball and socket joint ....

(ii) another hinge joint. ....(2 marks)

d) What are the three functions of the skeleton? (3 marks)

....

e) What are the names of the two muscles that bend and straighten the arm? (2 marks)

....

Score /10

How well did you do? 1–7 Try again 8–13 Getting there 14–22 Good work 23–30 Excellent!

The lungs and breathing

- The lungs are two big air sacs in your upper body.
- Their job is to supply oxygen to your cells when you breathe in and get rid of the waste product carbon dioxide when you breathe out.
- This is called gas exchange.

A Choose just one answer, a, b, c or d.

1 Where does gas exchange take place? (1 mark)
a) diaphragm   b) bronchi
c) trachea   d) alveoli

2 What is respiration? (1 mark)
a) breathing in
b) breathing out
c) a chemical reaction that uses glucose and oxygen
d) a plant's way of making food

3 What does your diaphragm do when you breathe in? (1 mark)
a) relaxes and moves up
b) moves down and relaxes
c) contracts and moves down
d) moves up and contracts

4 When you breathe in your ribs move: (1 mark)
a) down and in
b) up and out
c) up and in
d) down and out

5 Which gas do we breathe more in than out? (1 mark)
a) oxygen   b) carbon dioxide
c) water vapour   d) hydrogen

Score /5

B Answer all parts of all questions.

1 Write the numbers 1 to 5 next to the sentences to show the correct sequence of events when we breathe out. (5 marks)

The volume inside the chest decreases.   ....

Air is forced out of the lungs.   ....

The intercostal muscles relax.   ....

The ribs move down and in.   ....

The diaphragm relaxes.   ....

2 Name 3 other differences between the air we breathe out and the air we breathe in. (3 marks)

The air we breathe out contains more carbon dioxide, ...

....

....

3 Write out the parts of the breathing system in the order that oxygen passes through to get to the blood capillaries. (5 marks)

bronchioles   bronchi   trachea   alveoli   mouth

....

Score /13

C   This is a SATs-style question. Answer all parts of the question.

1 A piece of apparatus called a bell jar represents the breathing system.

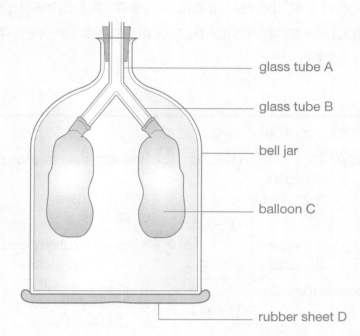

glass tube A

glass tube B

bell jar

balloon C

rubber sheet D

a) Put the letter of the part of the bell jar apparatus that represents the: (5 marks)

(i)   lungs   ....

(ii) ribs   ....

(iii) diaphragm   ....

(iv) trachea   ....

(v)   bronchi   ....

b) John's ribs move up and out and his diaphragm moves down when he breathes.
Is he breathing in or out when this happens?   (1 mark)

....

c) What happens to his ribs when he breathes out?   (1 mark)

....

d) Where in the lungs does oxygen pass into the blood?   (1 mark)

....

Score   /8

How well did you do?   1–7 Try again   8–12 Getting there   13–19 Good work   20–26 Excellent!

The menstrual cycle

Adolescence is a time in people's lives when the body changes from a child to an adult. Emotional and physical changes occur during puberty. The male and female reproductive systems undergo changes in preparation for the possibility of reproduction.

A Choose just one answer, a, b, c or d.

1 Where are sperm made? (1 mark)
a) testes   b) ovaries
c) penis   d) bladder

2 Where are eggs made? (1 mark)
a) testes   b) vagina
c) ovaries   d) uterus

3 How often does menstruation usually take place? (1 mark)
a) every 2 weeks   b) every 28 days
c) every six months   d) every year

4 How long does menstruation usually last?
(1 mark)
a) 10–15 days   b) 4–7 days
c) 28 days   d) 10–28 days

5 When does puberty usually begin? (1 mark)
a) 14–20 years old
b) 5–10 years old
c) 20–25 years old
d) 10–14 years old

Score /5

B Answer all parts of all questions.

1 Explain the meaning of the following terms: (4 marks)

puberty ....

menstruation ....

ovaries ....

testes ....

2 Fill in the gaps using the words provided. (7 marks)

28 days   day 14   4–7 days   ovulation   uterus lining   ovaries   period

During puberty females usually begin menstruation. This occurs approximately once every .... The cycle begins when alternate .... release an egg into the Fallopian tube. This happens on approximately .... of the cycle and is called ....

If the egg is not fertilised then menstruation begins. This consists of loss of the egg and the .... and is sometimes called a .... A period can last ....

Score /11

C This is a SATs-style question. Answer all parts of the question.

1 The diagram shows a section through the female reproductive system.

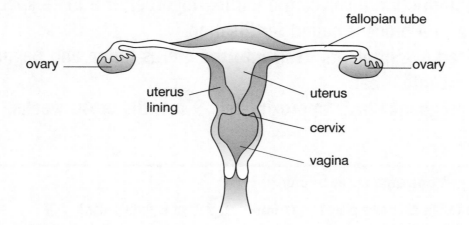

fallopian tube

ovary

ovary

uterus lining

uterus

cervix

vagina

a) In which parts are eggs made? (1 mark)

....

b) How often are eggs released from the female reproductive system? (1 mark)

....

c) In which part does fertilisation take place? (1 mark)

....

d) What happens if an egg is not fertilised? (1 mark)

....

e) Where are sperm made in the male reproductive system? (1 mark)

....

f) Toby has noticed that he has hair growing on his face and under his arms. His voice is also
starting to get deeper. What is the name of the process that is happening to Toby? (1 mark)

....

g) What chemicals cause these changes? (1 mark)

....

h) Name one other change that occurs during this time. (1 mark)

....

Score /8

How well did you do? 1–4 Try again 5–9 Getting there 10–16 Good work 17–24 Excellent!

Reproduction

- Human reproduction involves the joining together of a male sperm and a female egg in a process called fertilisation.
- The fertilised egg implants itself into the uterus lining and begins its development into a baby.
- A human pregnancy lasts approximately 9 months or 40 weeks.

A Choose just one answer, a, b, c or d.

1 Where does fertilisation take place? (1 mark)
   a) fallopian tube   b) uterus
   c) vagina   d) cervix

2 How is the baby provided with oxygen and nutrients? (1 mark)
   a) placenta   b) umbilical cord
   c) amniotic fluid   d) cervix

3 How long does a human pregnancy usually last? (1 mark)
   a) 6 months   b) 10 months
   c) 1 month   d) 9 months

4 What is fertilisation? (1 mark)
   a) the sperm's tail breaking off
   b) a sperm nucleus and egg nucleus fusing
   c) the sperm swimming towards the egg
   d) an egg released from the ovary

5 What is the placenta used for? (1 mark)
   a) protection against bangs
   b) make birth easier
   c) a barrier against harmful substances
   d) to produce red blood cells

Score   /5

B Answer all parts of all questions.

1 What is the name of the process when: (2 marks)

   a) an egg nucleus fuses with a sperm nucleus? ....

   b) a fertilised egg implants into the uterus wall? ....

2 Number the following stages to show the stages of childbirth. (5 marks)

Contractions push the placenta out.   ....

The uterus begins to contract.   ....

The cervix widens.   ....

The umbilical cord is cut.   ....

More contractions happen and the baby is born.   ....

3 Cross out one sentence to leave the correct explanation of how identical twins are formed. (1 mark)

One egg is fertilised by one sperm and divides into two.
Two eggs are fertilised by two sperm.

Score   /8

C This is a SATs-style question. Answer all parts of the question.

1 The diagram shows a baby developing in its mother's uterus.

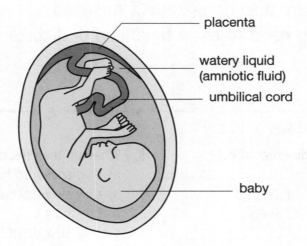

placenta

watery liquid
(amniotic fluid)

umbilical cord

baby

a) How long does a human pregnancy usually last? (1 mark)

....

b) Through which labelled part can harmful substances pass between the mother's blood
and the baby's blood? (1 mark)

....

c) Name a harmful substance that may be passed from the mother's blood to the
baby's blood. (1 mark)

....

d) Describe how the baby receives food and oxygen whilst in the mother's uterus. Use
words from the diagram. (2 marks)

....

....

e) What is the function of the amniotic fluid? (1 mark)

....

f) What happens to the placenta after the baby is born? (2 marks)

....

Score   /8

How well did you do?   1–4 Try again   5–9 Getting there   10–16 Good work   17–21 Excellent!

Drugs

- Without a doubt, smoking and solvents damage health.
- Alcohol and drugs are also dangerous if misused.
- To keep healthy you need to eat a balanced diet, take regular exercise and avoid health risks.

A — Choose just one answer, a, b, c or d.

1 Which part of the body do drugs affect the most? **(1 mark)**
a) skeleton   b) brain
c) blood vessels d) lungs

2 Alcohol is: **(1 mark)**
a) a depressant   b) a painkiller
c) a stimulant   d) a hallucinogen

3 Alcohol can cause a disease of which organ? **(1 mark)**
a) brain   b) lungs
c) heart   d) liver

4 What are the effects of solvents? **(1 mark)**
a) they speed up heart and breathing rates
b) they slow down the heart but speed up breathing
c) they slow down heart and breathing rates
d) they speed up the heart but slow down breathing rate

5 Smoking can cause a disease called: **(1 mark)**
a) bronchitis   b) cirrhosis
c) rickets   d) cholera

Score /5

B — Answer all parts of all questions.

1 Match up these facts with the following drugs. **(7 marks)**

sedative   hallucinogen   painkiller   stimulant   alcohol   solvent   cigarette

A depressant that slows the body's reactions. It causes a disease called cirrhosis. ....

It contains many harmful chemical substances and is very addictive. It contributes to a disease called emphysema. ....

This drug can give you extreme energy and also dehydration. It causes you to imagine things that are not really there. ....

It slows down the brain and alters reaction times. It can be used to treat stress and anxiety. ....

It speeds up the brain and nervous system, addiction is high and withdrawal has many side effects including depression. ....

This drug is used to treat pain. Misuse can lead to infectious diseases and it is extremely addictive. ....

This drug affects the lungs, brain, kidneys and liver. It can cause loss of control and unconsciousness. ....

2 Explain what is meant by saying drugs have side effects, and give some examples. **(3 marks)**

....

....

Score /10

C These are SATs-style questions. Answer all parts of the questions.

1 Look at the graph below.

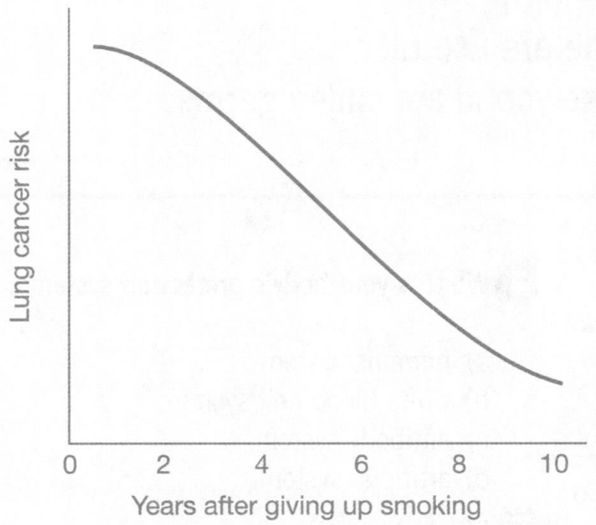

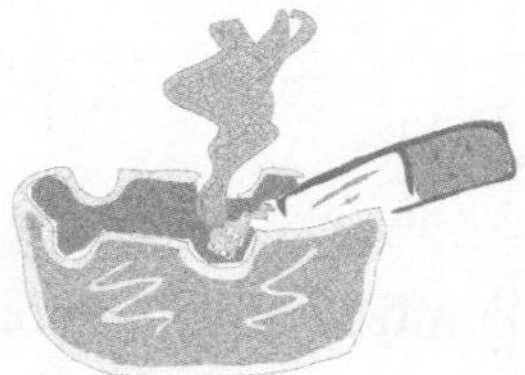

a) Using the graph, describe how giving up smoking affects the chance of getting lung cancer. (2 marks)

....

....

b) Smoking contains many substances; the following are just three of them: (3 marks)

nicotine   tar   carbon monoxide

(i) Which is a mixture that contains chemicals that cause cancer? ....

(ii) Which prevents your blood from carrying as much oxygen? ....

(iii) Which is an addictive substance? ....

2 a) Alcohol is a drug. Which of the two following statements are true about alcohol? Tick the correct boxes. (2 marks)

- Alcohol is a stimulant. ☐
- Alcohol is a depressant. ☐
- Alcohol affects the liver. ☐
- Alcohol affects the lungs. ☐

b) Which other organ of the body is affected by alcohol? (1 mark)

....

Score /8

How well did you do? 1–4 Try again 5–9 Getting there 10–16 Good work 17–23 Excellent!

For more help on this topic see KS3 Science Success Guide pages 24–25

Fighting disease

- Microbes are bacteria, viruses and fungi.
- Not all microbes cause disease; some are useful.
- Microbes that get inside you and make you ill are called germs.

A Choose just one answer, a, b, c or d.

1 Which type of microbe causes athlete's foot?

(1 mark)

a) fungi   b) bacteria
c) virus   d) none of them

2 Which type of cell produces antibodies?

(1 mark)

a) red blood cells   b) bacteria
c) virus   d) white blood cells

3 Which part of your body stops microbes from entering?

(1 mark)

a) stomach   b) blood
c) mouth   d) skin

4 What is your body's protection system called?

(1 mark)

a) immune system
b) white blood cell system
c) antibody system
d) artificial system

5 What are vaccines?   (1 mark)

a) a collection of white blood cells
b) dead/harmless microbes
c) antibodies
d) a selection of toxins

Score   /5

B Answer all parts of all questions.

1 Put a tick or a cross in the box by each statement to indicate whether or not it is correct.   (5 marks)

Fungi cause a disease called athlete's foot.   ☐

Viruses are larger than bacteria.   ☐

All bacteria are harmful.   ☐

White blood cells produce antibodies.   ☐

A vaccine gives a person natural immunity.   ☐

2 Do bacteria, viruses or fungi cause the following diseases?   (5 marks)

athlete's foot   ....   HIV   ....

tuberculosis   ....   chicken pox   ....

food poisoning   ....

3 Match the description of how these white blood cells work to the picture.   (2 marks)

- This type of white blood cell makes antibodies to fight microbes.
- This type of white blood cell engulfs bacteria or viruses.

Score   /12

C This is a SATs-style question. Answer all parts of the question.

1 Below is a diagram of a bacterial cell that can cause disease.

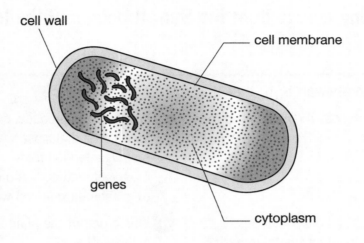

cell wall

cell membrane

genes

cytoplasm

a) Give one difference between the bacterial cell and a typical animal cell.   (1 mark)

....

b) Some bacteria are useful, but some cause disease if they enter the body. List three ways
in which bacteria can enter the body.   (3 marks)

....

....

....

c) Which type of cell helps our body fight disease?   (1 mark)

....

d) Sometimes harmful bacteria enter your body but you don't get any symptoms of the disease.
This can be through natural immunity or artificial immunity. What is natural immunity?   (2 marks)

....

....

e) Name a disease caused by bacteria.   (1 mark)

....

Score   /8

How well did you do?   1–6 Try again   7–12 Getting there   13–18 Good work   19–25 Excellent!

For more help on this topic see KS3 Science Success Guide pages 4 & 26–27

29

Photosynthesis

Photosynthesis is a chemical process that plants use to make their food (glucose) using energy from the Sun. It occurs in the leaves.

A Choose just one answer, a, b, c or d.

1 Which of these substances do plants need for photosynthesis? **(1 mark)**
a) oxygen
b) glucose
c) carbon dioxide
d) pollen

2 What else do plants need for photosynthesis? **(1 mark)**
a) water and oxygen
b) oxygen and glucose
c) water and light
d) oxygen and light

3 What are the products of photosynthesis? **(1 mark)**
a) water and glucose
b) oxygen and glucose
c) oxygen and carbon dioxide
d) carbon dioxide and water

4 Which part of the plant carries out photosynthesis? **(1 mark)**
a) leaf   b) flower
c) root   d) stem

5 What substance do plants store glucose as?
a) sugar   **(1 mark)**
b) glycogen
c) starch
d) oxygen

Score   /5

B Answer all parts of all questions.

1 Match the part of the leaf with its function. **(3 marks)**

Xylem	transport of glucose up and down the plant
Phloem	diffusion of carbon dioxide and oxygen in and out of the leaf
Stomata	transport of water from the roots to the leaves

2 Number the stages to show the correct sequence when testing a leaf for starch. **(5 marks)**

Put the leaf in a test tube of ethanol and stand in hot water for 10 mins. ....

Lay the leaf flat in a petri dish and add iodine solution. ....

Dip a leaf in boiling water to soften it. ....

Wash the leaf. ....

The leaf goes blue/black in colour if starch is present. ....

3 Put these words in the correct column to show if they are needed for photosynthesis or produced by photosynthesis. **(6 marks)**

glucose   chlorophyll   oxygen   water   light   carbon dioxide

Needed	Produced

Score   /14

These are SATs-style questions. Answer all parts of the questions.

1 The picture shows an apple tree.

a) The apple tree takes in water from the soil. Name one other substance the tree must get from the soil. (1 mark)

....

b) In order to make its own food, the apple tree also needs another substance from the air. Name this substance. (1 mark)

....

c) What is the name of the process that the tree uses to make its food? (1 mark)

....

d) In the winter the apple tree loses its leaves. Explain why this prevents the apple tree from growing. (1 mark)

....

2 The picture shows a plant grown in the middle of the garden and a plant grown underneath a tree.

a) Explain why the plant grown under the tree is smaller than the other plant. (1 mark)

....

b) Give one other reason why the plant under the tree may be smaller than the other plant. (1 mark)

....

Score /6

How well did you do? 1–6 Try again 7–12 Getting there 13–18 Good work 19–25 Excellent!

PHOTOSYNTHESIS **Biology**

Plant reproduction

- Plants have male and female sex cells just like animals.
- They reproduce by forming seeds inside fruits.
- Reproduction consists of pollination, fertilisation, seed dispersal and germination.

A
Choose just one answer, a, b, c or d.

1 Which is the male sex cell in plants? **(1 mark)**
a) ovule   b) pollen
c) anther   d) filament

2 Which of these is the female sex cell? **(1 mark)**
a) ovary   b) anther
c) pollen   d) ovule

3 Which stage is the beginning of fertilisation?
a) a pollen tube beginning to grow   **(1 mark)**
b) ovary turns into a fruit
c) pollen lands on the stigma
d) ovule grows into a seed

4 Which of these conditions is not suitable for germination?   **(1 mark)**
a) warmth   b) moisture
c) cold   d) oxygen

5 Which of these is not a method of seed dispersal?   **(1 mark)**
a) fog
b) wind
c) animals
d) popping out

Score   /5

B
Answer all parts of all questions.

1 Put an F by the part if you think it is female and an M if you think it is male.   **(9 marks)**

anther   ....   ovary   ....

stigma   ....   filament   ....

style   ....   carpel   ....

stamen   ....   pollen   ....

svule   ....

2 Cross out the incorrect words in this passage about the making of a seed.   **(8 marks)**

To begin the process of making a seed a pollen grain must land on the stigma/style of the plant. This can happen on the same plant, when it is called self-pollination/cross-pollination, or between two plants, when it is called self-pollination/cross-pollination. Wind or animals help transfer the pollen.

Once the pollen grain has landed, a tube begins to grow down the style/filament. A pollen grain nucleus moves down this tube towards the ovary/stigma. Fertilisation/pollination occurs when the pollen nucleus joins with the ovule nucleus. The ovary turns into a seed/fruit and the ovule grows into a fruit/seed.

Score   /17

C This is a SATs-style question. Answer all parts of the question.

1 The diagram below shows a flower that has been cut in half to show its reproductive organs.

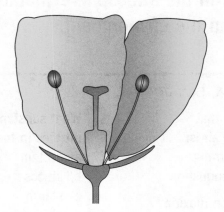

a) Label with the letter A the part of the flower that produces seeds.   (2 marks)

b) Label with the letter B the part of the flower that produces pollen.

c) A bee with pollen on it from one flower lands on the stigma of another flower.
What is this called?   (1 mark)

....

d) Name another way that pollen may be transferred from flower to flower.   (1 mark)

....

e) Once the pollen lands on the stigma a tube grows down towards the ovule in the ovary.
The pollen nucleus travels down this tube to join with the ovule nucleus. What is this
process called?   (1 mark)

....

f) The seeds produced by the flower need to be scattered over a large area in order to grow
into new plants. Give two ways that this can happen.   (2 marks)

....

g) The seeds need oxygen and warmth so they can germinate. What other important
substance is needed?   (1 mark)

....

Score   /8

For more help on this topic see KS3 Science Success Guide pages 30–31

Carbon and nitrogen cycles

- Carbon dioxide and nitrogen are atmospheric gases.
- The amount of each gas in the atmosphere should stay the same, as they are constantly recycled in the environment.

A Choose just one answer, a, b, c or d.

1 One process in the carbon cycle that absorbs carbon dioxide from the air is: (1 mark)
   a) photosynthesis   b) burning
   c) respiration   d) combustion

2 One process that releases carbon dioxide to the air is: (1 mark)
   a) photosynthesis   b) feeding
   c) moving   d) respiration

3 Which organisms carry out respiration? (1 mark)
   a) plants   b) humans
   c) bacteria and fungi   d) all of them

4 What substance do plants make from nitrates in the soil? (1 mark)
   a) protein
   b) glucose
   c) starch
   d) glycogen

5 How do animals first get nitrogen compounds into their bodies? (1 mark)
   a) by hibernating
   b) by respiration
   c) by eating plants
   d) by photosynthesis

Score /5

B Answer all parts of all questions.

1 What are decomposers? (2 marks)

....

....

2 There are two ways carbon dioxide can be released into the atmosphere. They are respiration and burning (combustion). Complete this word equation for respiration. (2 marks)

Fuel (glucose) + ... ⇨ carbon dioxide + water + ...

3 Complete this word equation for burning. (2 marks)

.... + oxygen ⇨ carbon dioxide + ... + energy

4 What do you notice about the two equations? (2 marks)

....

5 Photosynthesis takes carbon dioxide from the atmosphere. Complete this word equation for photosynthesis. (2 marks)

Carbon dioxide + ... ⇨ glucose + ... + energy

6 What do you notice about the equations for respiration and photosynthesis? (2 marks)

....

....

Score /12

34

C   These are SATs-style questions. Answer all parts of the questions.

1 The diagram shows a very simplified version of the carbon cycle.

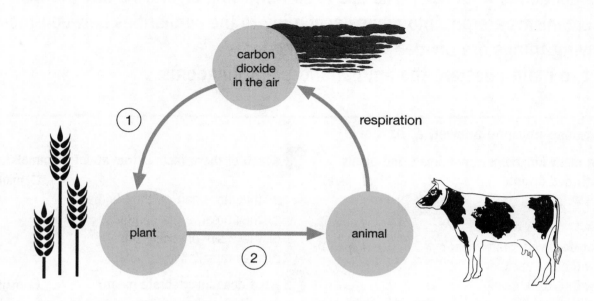

a) Name the processes numbered 1 and 2 on the diagram.   (2 marks)

1 ....

2 ....

b) Name another way that carbon dioxide can be released into the air.   (1 mark)

....

c) What happens to the carbon in animal and plant bodies when they die or produce waste? (2 marks)

....

d) What happens to animals and plants that do not decay?   (1 mark)

....

2 The Nitrogen Cycle is an important way of getting nitrogen compounds into the bodies of plants and animals.

a) What do animals and plants need nitrogen for?   (1 mark)

....

b) Is there more carbon dioxide or nitrogen present in the air?   (1 mark)

....

Score   /8

How well did you do?   1–6 Try again   7–12 Getting there   13–18 Good work   19–25 Excellent!

Classification

- Classification is what scientists use to sort all living organisms into groups.
- The organisms are put into groups according to the similarities between them.
- All living things are divided first into kingdoms.
- The two main ones are the animal and plant kingdoms.

A Choose just one answer, a, b, c or d.

1 How many kingdoms can animals and plants be divided up into? **(1 mark)**
a) 3   b) 4
c) 2   d) 1

2 What does vertebrate mean? **(1 mark)**
a) without a backbone
b) with a backbone
c) with scales   d) without scales

3 Which is the odd one out? **(1 mark)**
a) fish   b) mammal
c) worm   d) bird

4 Which of these facts is true about mammals? **(1 mark)**
a) they have hair on their bodies
b) they breathe through gills
c) they have dry scaly skin
d) they mostly live in water

5 What does invertebrate mean? **(1 mark)**
a) without a backbone
b) with a backbone
c) with scales
d) without scales

Score   /5

B Answer all parts of all questions.

1 Which of the following plants is the odd one out? **(2 marks)**

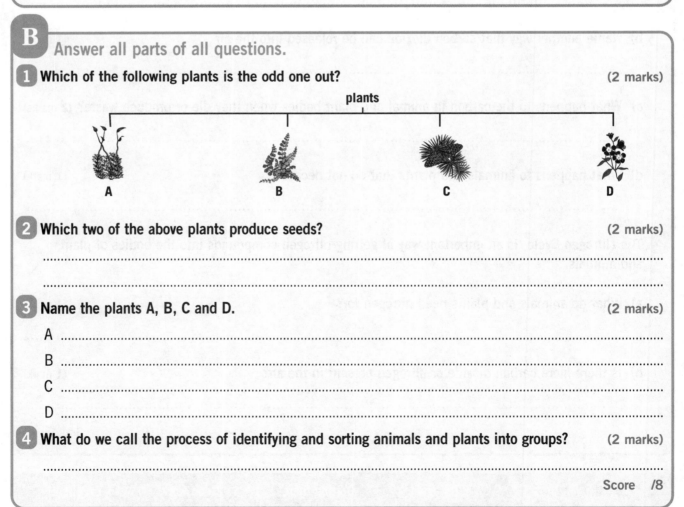

plants

A   B   C   D

2 Which two of the above plants produce seeds? **(2 marks)**

....

....

3 Name the plants A, B, C and D. **(2 marks)**

A ....

B ....

C ....

D ....

4 What do we call the process of identifying and sorting animals and plants into groups? **(2 marks)**

....

Score   /8

C This is a SATs-style question. Answer all parts of the question.

1 The diagrams show an animal from each of the vertebrate groups.

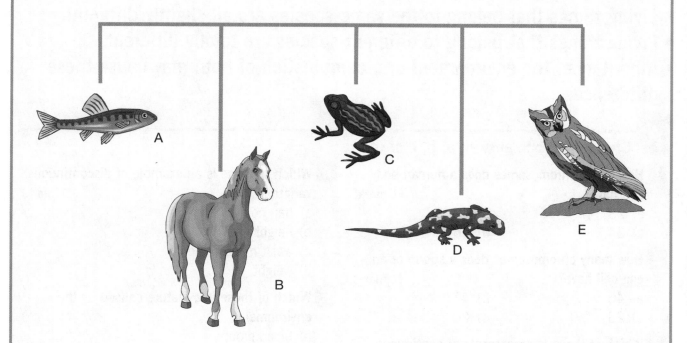

a) **Match up the letters to the correct vertebrate group.** (5 marks)

- mammal ....
- bird ....
- fish ....
- amphibian ....
- reptile ....

b) **What does vertebrate mean?** (1 mark)

....

c) **Which vertebrate group can only live in water?** (1 mark)

....

d) **Which vertebrate group lives on land and in water but breeds in water?** (1 mark)

....

Score /8

How well did you do? 1–4 **Try again** 5–9 **Getting there** 10–16 **Good work** 17–21 **Excellent!**

Variation

- All living things vary in the way they look or behave.
- Living things that belong to the same species are all slightly different.
- Living things that belong to different species are totally different.
- Inheritance, the environment or a combination of both may cause these differences.

A Choose just one answer, a, b, c or d.

1 How many chromosomes does a human body cell have? (1 mark)
- a) 23
- b) 47
- c) 24
- d) 46

2 How many chromosomes does a sperm or an egg cell have? (1 mark)
- a) 46
- b) 47
- c) 23
- d) 20

3 Which of these is an example of continuous variation? (1 mark)
- a) rolling tongues
- b) blood group
- c) hair colour
- d) foot size

4 Which of these is an example of discontinuous variation? (1 mark)
- a) hair colour
- b) height
- c) waist measurement
- d) weight

5 Which of these is a feature caused by the environment? (1 mark)
- a) blood group
- b) scars
- c) eye colour
- d) natural hair colour

Score   /5

B Answer all parts of all questions.

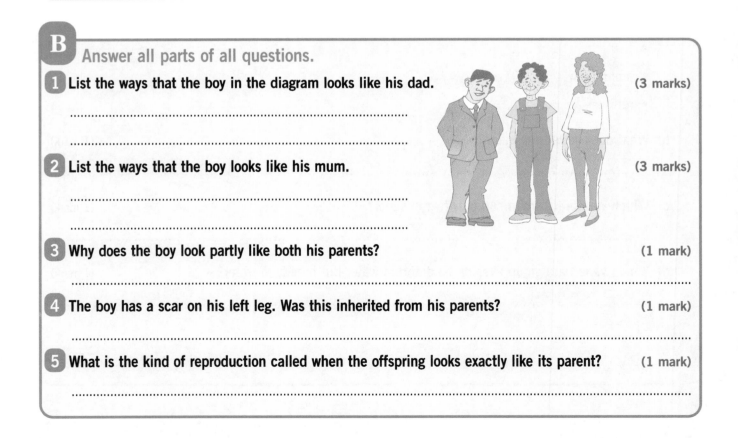

1 List the ways that the boy in the diagram looks like his dad. (3 marks)

....

....

2 List the ways that the boy looks like his mum. (3 marks)

....

....

3 Why does the boy look partly like both his parents? (1 mark)

....

4 The boy has a scar on his left leg. Was this inherited from his parents? (1 mark)

....

5 What is the kind of reproduction called when the offspring looks exactly like its parent? (1 mark)

....

B (Continued)

6 The following is a list of features. Put an **I** if you think it is inherited and an **E** if you think it is caused by the environment. **(5 marks)**

eye colour	....	scars	....
blood group	....	hair length	....
ability to roll tongue	....		

Score   /14

C

This is a SATs-style question. Answer all parts of the question.

1 The following table shows the hair colour of a class of pupils in Ashford Junior School.

Hair colour	Number
brown	8
black	4
blond	6
ginger	4

a) Draw a bar chart of this information. **(4 marks)**

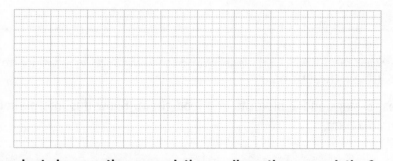

b) Does the bar chart show continuous variation or discontinuous variation? **(1 mark)**

....

c) Why do people have different natural hair colours? **(1 mark)**

....

d) Give an example of continuous variation. **(1 mark)**

....

e) Cuttings were taken from a rose bush and planted in two different gardens. When they grew they looked different. Why do they look different? **(1 mark)**

....

Score   /8

How well did you do?   1–7 Try again   8–12 Getting there   13–19 Good work   20–27 Excellent!

For more help on this topic see KS3 Science Success Guide pages 36–37

Food chains and webs

• Food chains and webs begin with energy from the Sun.

A Choose just one answer, a, b, c or d.

1 What do food chains show? (1 mark)
a) what eats what in a simple feeding relationship
b) the numbers involved in a simple feeding relationship
c) how much animals and plants eat
d) the feeding times of animals and plants

2 What is a producer? (1 mark)
a) an animal that eats plants
b) a green plant
c) an animal that eats meat
d) an animal that produces food

3 What is a herbivore? (1 mark)
a) an animal that eats only meat
b) an animal that eats meat and plants
c) an animal that eats only plants
d) a plant

4 What is a carnivore? (1 mark)
a) an animal that eats only plants
b) an animal that eats only meat
c) an animal that eats meat and plants
d) a plant

5 What is a food web? (1 mark)
a) a series of linked food chains
b) a complicated food chain
c) it shows the numbers in a food chain
d) it shows the mass in a food chain

Score /5

B Answer all parts of all questions.

1 There are 10 lettuces, 5 slugs and 2 blue tits in a food chain. Show this information in a pyramid of numbers diagram. (3 marks)

2 Give a definition of the following terms. (4 marks)

Producer ....

Herbivore ....

Carnivore ....

Food chain ....

B (Continued)

3 Draw a food chain linking the following organisms. (2 marks)

earthworm   oak leaves   hedgehog   fox

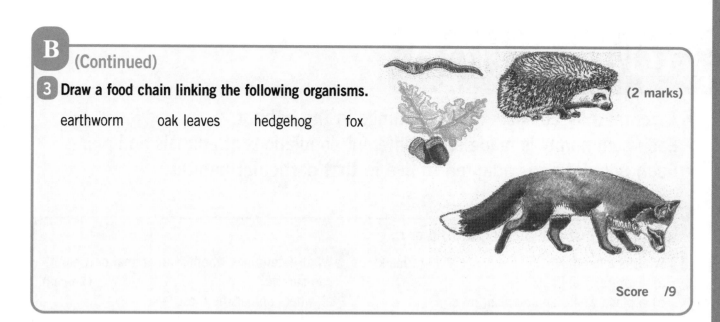

Score /9

C

This is a SATs-style question. Answer all parts of the question.

1 Look at this food chain.

Rose bush ⇨ Greenfly ⇨ Ladybird ⇨ Thrush

a) Which is the producer in this food chain? (1 mark)

....

b) Which are the predators in this food chain? (2 marks)

....

c) Why do rose bushes grow better if there are lots of ladybirds in the garden? (1 mark)

....

d) One year the rose bushes became infected by a disease and there were fewer of them. What were the effects on the rest of the food chain? (2 marks)

....

....

e) What is the source of energy in a food chain? (1 mark)

....

f) Many food chains linked together show a more realistic picture of what eats what. What are linked food chains called? (1 mark)

....

Score /8

How well did you do?   1–4 Try again   5–8 Getting there   9–15 Good work   16–22 Excellent!

For more help on this topic see KS3 Science Success Guide pages 38–39

Adaptation

- A community consists of living things in the habitat.
- Each community is made up of different populations of animals and plants.
- Each population is adapted to live in that particular habitat.

A Choose just one answer, a, b, c or d.

1 **What is a habitat?** (1 mark)
- a) a group of animals
- b) a place where an organism lives
- c) a group of plants
- d) where only decomposers live

2 **Which of these is an adaptation of a polar bear?**
- a) it produces little urine (1 mark)
- b) it does not sweat
- c) it can store water
- d) it has a thick coat

3 **What is a predator?** (1 mark)
- a) the hunted animal
- b) a green plant
- c) an animal that hunts
- d) an animal that eats plants

4 **What determines whether an animal or a plant can survive?** (1 mark)
- a) what can eat the most
- b) whether it is adapted to its environment
- c) the tallest animal or plant
- d) the biggest animal or plant

5 **Why do the numbers of animals or plants remain fairly constant?** (1 mark)
- a) because of the predator–prey cycle
- b) because they stop eating eventually
- c) the prey eat all the predators
- d) the predators eat all the prey

Score   /5

B Answer all parts of all questions.

1 Look at the picture of the polar bear. List as many examples as you can of ways the polar bear has adapted to living in cold arctic regions. (4 marks)

....

....

....

2 Weeds like the dandelion compete with other plants for light, space and water. The dandelion is a very successful weed. The following is a list of features of the dandelion. For each one explain how it helps the dandelion survive. (4 marks)

a) Its leaves are spread flat against the ground.

....

b) It produces many seeds.

....

c) It has very deep roots.

....

d) Its seeds germinate rapidly.

....

Score   /8

42

C These are SATs-style questions. Answer all parts of the questions.

The drawing below shows a fish.

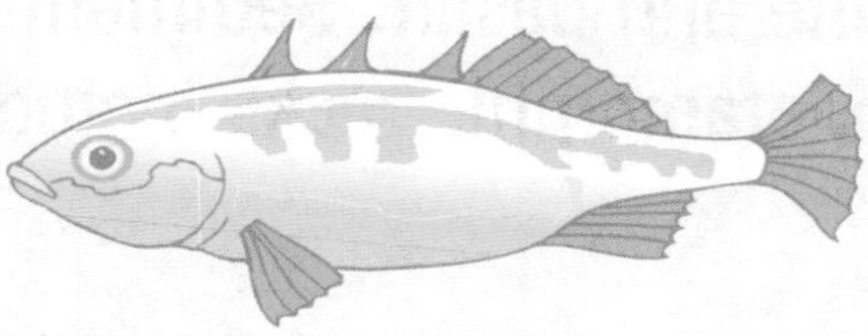

1 Describe ways in which the fish is adapted to live in water. (3 marks)

....

....

....

2 Look at the diagram of a predator–prey graph.

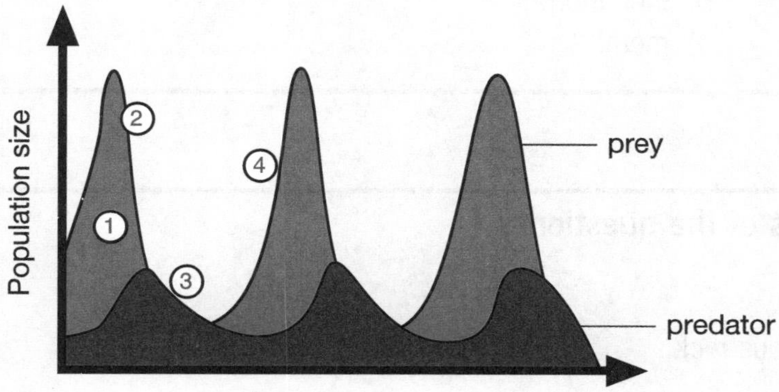

a) Explain briefly why the number of prey falls when the number of predators rises. (1 mark)

....

b) Name a predator and its prey whose relationship could be represented by the graph above. (2 marks)

....

....

c) How have prey adapted to avoid being killed by predators? (2 marks)

....

....

Score /8

How well did you do? 1–4 Try again 5–9 Getting there 10–16 Good work 17–21 Excellent!

For more help on this topic see KS3 Science Success Guide pages 40–41

Rocks

There are three types of rock – igneous, sedimentary and metamorphic. Igneous rocks include granite and basalt. Sedimentary rocks include limestone and sandstone. Metamorphic rocks include schist and gneiss.

A Choose just one answer, a, b, c or d.

1 Over what sort of time period do sedimentary rocks form? (1 mark)
a) thousands of years b) millions of years
c) a fortnight d) tens of years

2 Which of these is NOT a type of rock? (1 mark)
a) sedimentary b) igneous
c) crystal d) metamorphic

3 What is the hardest type of rock? (1 mark)
a) igneous b) metamorphic
c) sedimentary d) metal

4 Which type of rock contains bands of crystals?
a) mineral b) igneous (1 mark)
c) sedimentary d) metamorphic

5 Sedimentary rocks tend to be: (1 mark)
a) quite hard b) very hard
c) crumbly d) green

Score /5

B Answer all parts of the questions.

1 True or false? (5 marks)

a) Basalt is an igneous rock.

b) Sedimentary rocks may contain fossils.

c) Limestone is a metamorphic rock.

d) Magma cools down and crystallises to form sedimentary rocks.

e) Metamorphic rocks are formed by high temperatures and pressures on existing rocks.

2 Each of these sentences contains a mistake. Rewrite the sentence without the mistake. (5 marks)

a) Sedimentary rocks are harder than igneous rocks.

b) At least 5% of any limestone rock is calcium carbonate.

c) Slate is an igneous rock.

d) Metamorphic rocks are formed by low temperatures and pressures on existing rocks.

e) Igneous rocks may have bands of crystals.

Score /10

C

This is a SATs-style question. Answer all parts of the question.

1 The cross section below shows the different rocks that were found in a cliff face.

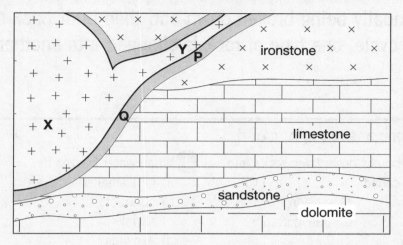

X represents part of a large igneous intrusion and Y represents a smaller igneous intrusion called a sill.

a) Some rocks contain fossils. What is a fossil? (1 mark)

....

b) In which type of rock is a fossil most likely to be found? (1 mark)

....

c) In which type of rock are fossils never found? (1 mark)

....

Both the rocks found at X and Y contain crystals. The crystals at Y formed more quickly than the crystals at X.

d) Where are the larger crystals found? (1 mark)

....

e) What type of rock is limestone? (1 mark)

....

f) What type of rock is formed around the outside of the igneous intrusions X and Y? (1 mark)

....

g) Why is the rock formed at Q different from the rock formed at P? (1 mark)

....

Score   /7

How well did you do?   ✗ 1–4 **Try again**   5–9 **Getting there**   10–16 **Good work**   17–22 **Excellent!** ✓

The rock cycle

Rocks are continually being broken down and then built back up again. During the rock cycle, one type of rock is changed into another.

A   Choose just one answer, a, b, c or d.

1 The process that breaks down large rocks into smaller pieces is called: **(1 mark)**
a) deposition   b) erosion
c) weathering   d) transportation

2 Physical weathering involves changes in: **(1 mark)**
a) colour   b) temperature
c) rock   d) time

3 Freeze–thaw weathering involves: **(1 mark)**
a) sulphur dioxide   b) acid rain
c) pollution   d) water

4 When water freezes it: **(1 mark)**
a) gets smaller
b) contracts
c) shrinks
d) expands

5 Which type of rock is *not* attacked by acid rain? **(1 mark)**
a) granite
b) limestone
c) chalk
d) marble

Score   /5

B   Answer all parts of the question.

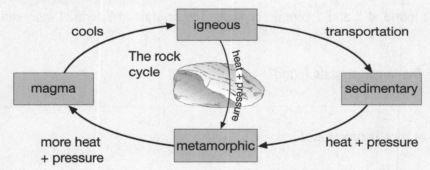

1 a) When molten rock cools it forms .... rocks. Rocks formed slowly below the surface of the Earth are called .... rocks. Those formed more quickly at the Earth's surface in contact with the air or with water are called .... rocks. At the Earth's surface rocks are weathered. Weathering breaks down big rocks into .... pieces. **(4 marks)**

b) Sedimentary rocks are formed from layers of .... laid down in lakes or seas. As more layers of sediment build up, water is gradually squeezed out of the sediments. Eventually the rock grains become .... together to form sedimentary rocks. These rocks may contain .... **(3 marks)**

c) High temperatures and .... can turn existing sedimentary or .... rocks into metamorphic rocks. Examples of .... rocks include schist, gneiss and slate. **(3 marks)**

Score   /10

C These are SATs-style questions. Answer all parts of the questions.

1 Sedimentary rocks like limestone are often porous.

a) What substance can enter into the gaps between the grains in limestone? (1 mark)

....

b) What does the substance form when it freezes? (1 mark)

....

c) How does this cause the limestone to be broken down? (1 mark)

....

....

....

2 A number of events are listed below. Place these events in order to show how granite can be changed into a sedimentary rock. (6 marks)

The water is squeezed out of the sediment and the rock grains become cemented together.

Granite is weathered.

The river deposits the sediment.

Layers of sediment build up.

The weathered rock pieces are transported by rivers.

The river flows more slowly as it reaches the sea.

1st event ....

2nd event..

3rd event..

4th event..

5th event..

6th event..

Score /9

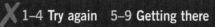

Pollution

The atmosphere around us is very precious. To protect it we need to understand how it may become polluted.

A Choose just one answer, a, b, c or d.

1 Which of these elements may be found in fossil fuels? **(1 mark)**
a) sulphur   b) nitrogen
c) helium   d) calcium

2 Which of these rocks does NOT contain calcium carbonate? **(1 mark)**
a) chalk   b) marble
c) sandstone   d) limestone

3 What type of solution is formed when sulphur dioxide dissolves in water? **(1 mark)**
a) acid   b) neutral
c) alkaline   d) limewater

4 Which of these substances can be formed by burning fossil fuels? **(1 mark)**
a) sodium chloride
b) carbon dioxide
c) sulphur
d) oxygen

5 Which compound causes the Greenhouse Effect? **(1 mark)**
a) water
b) sulphur dioxide
c) CFCs
d) carbon dioxide

Score /5

B Answer all parts of all questions.

1 Complete the passage below. **(5 marks)**

Sulphur is found in some fossil .... When substances burn they react with the oxygen in the air. The compounds formed are called oxides. When sulphur burns in air it forms ....

dioxide. Sulphur dioxide is soluble. This means that it .... in water.

If sulphur dioxide is released into the atmosphere it can dissolve in rainwater to form acid ....

Normally rainwater is slightly acidic because some carbon dioxide will have dissolved in it.

However, if sulphur dioxide is present the pH of the solution is even ....

2 Match the pollutant to the name of the problem that it causes and the effect that it has on the environment. **(2 marks)**

Name of pollutant	Name of problem	Effect on environment
carbon dioxide	acid rain	ice caps may melt as temperature rises
sulphur dioxide	greenhouse effect	damage to trees and statues

Score /7

C This is a SATs-style question. Answer all parts of the question.

1 a) Name the gas that found in polluted areas which causes acid rain. (1 mark)

....

b) How is the gas above formed? (1 mark)

....

....

c) Give one effect of acid rain. (1 mark)

....

....

....

2 a) Name the gas associated with global warming. (1 mark)

....

b) Give one possible effect of global warming. (1 mark)

....

....

....

3 If you saw lichen growing on a wall, what would this tell you about the air quality in the area?

(1 mark)

....

....

....

Score /6

How well did you do? ✗ 1–4 **Try again**   5–9 **Getting there**   10–13 **Good work**   14–28 **Excellent!** ✓

For more information on this topic, see pages 48–49 of your Success Guide.

49

States of matter

There are three states of matter – solid, liquid and gas.

A Choose just one answer, a, b, c or d.

1 How are the particles arranged in solids?

(1 mark)

a) close together   b) very far apart
c) fairly well separated d) fairly close together

2 How do the particles in a liquid move? (1 mark)

a) relative to each other, so liquids can flow
b) very quickly, in all directions
c) they vibrate about fixed positions
d) they cannot move

3 Which state of matter has the strongest forces of attraction between particles? (1 mark)

a) gas   b) liquid
c) solid   d) steam

4 Which state of matter has a definite volume, but does not have a definite shape? (1 mark)

a) gas
b) solid
c) steel
d) liquid

5 Which state of matter is the easiest to compress? (1 mark)

a) liquid
b) water
c) solid
d) gas

Score   /5

B Answer all parts of the questions.

1 Complete the table below to show the state of each of the elements shown at room temperature (25°C).

(3 marks)

Element	Melting point (degrees C)	Boiling point (degrees C)	State at room temperature
Chlorine	−101	−35	
Bromine	−7	59	
Rubidium	39	686	

2 Complete the sentences below.

(11 marks)

In a solid the .... are close together. They have fixed positions, but they do ....
When a solid is heated the particles move .... so they take up .... space.

The particles in a .... are quite close together, but they do move relative to each other. This means that liquids have a fixed .... but not a fixed shape. When a liquid is heated the particles move around more so the liquid .... Liquids expand more than .... on heating.

The particles in a .... are far apart and moving very .... in all directions. A .... will fill any container in which it is placed.

Score   /14

C These are SATs-style questions. Answer all parts of the questions.

1 The diagram opposite shows a metal ball and ring. At the start of the experiment the metal ball can pass though the ring. The teacher then carefully heats the metal ball using a Bunsen burner. After heating, the ball no longer fits through the ring.

ball and ring

a) What happened to the metal ball when it was heated? (1 mark)

....

b) What will happen to the ball as it cools down? (1 mark)

....

2 The table below shows the melting points and boiling points of four elements.

Element	Melting point (°C)	Boiling point (°C)
Manganese	1244	1962
Mercury	−39	357
Xenon	−112	−107
Iodine	114	184

a) Which of the elements shown in the table is a gas at room temperature? (1 mark)

....

b) Which of the elements shown in the table is a liquid at room temperature? (1 mark)

....

If the element manganese is heated it can change from a solid to a liquid and eventually to a gas. In which state is manganese when:

c) The atoms are far apart and moving very quickly in all directions? (1 mark)

....

d) The atoms are very close together and vibrate about fixed positions? (1 mark)

....

e) The atoms are quite close together but able to move past each other? (1 mark)

....

A sample of manganese is heated until it melts.

f) What is the change of state that has taken place? (1 mark)

....

Score /8

How well did you do? ✗ 1–7 Try again 8–12 Getting there 13–19 Good work 20–27 Excellent!

For more information on this topic, see pages 50–51 of your Success Guide.

Dissolving

If a solid dissolves in a liquid it forms a solution. Even though we can no longer see the solid it is still there, so the overall mass stays the same.

A Choose just one answer, a, b, c or d.

1 Which term can be used to describe a salt which can dissolve in water? **(1 mark)**
a) solvent
b) soluble
c) melted
d) insoluble

2 If salt is dissolved in water, how can the water be described? **(1 mark)**
a) a solution
b) a solute
c) soluble
d) a solvent

3 What is formed when a solid dissolves in a liquid? **(1 mark)**
a) a solution
b) a solute
c) a solvent
d) insoluble

4 Will hot or cold coffee dissolve more sugar?
a) it depends on the type of sugar **(1 mark)**
b) cold coffee
c) hot coffee
d) it depends on the type of coffee

5 Chalk does NOT dissolve in water. How can the chalk be described? **(1 mark)**
a) soluble
b) insoluble
c) a solute
d) melted

Score /5

B Answer all parts of the question.

1 Consider the following statements and decide whether each one is true or false.

a) Salt dissolves in water to form a solution. **(1 mark)**

....

b) Copper sulphate is insoluble. **(1 mark)**

....

c) Copper sulphate is insoluble in water. **(1 mark)**

....

d) Sugar is more soluble in hot water than in cold water. **(1 mark)**

....

e) Most solutes are more soluble at higher temperatures. **(1 mark)**

....

f) When no more solute can dissolve in a solution it has formed a saturated solution. **(1 mark)**

....

g) If 2g of a solute is dissolved in 100g of solvent the resultant solution will have a mass of 102g. **(1 mark)**

....

Score /7

C This is a SATs-style question. Answer all parts of the question.

1 Harry dissolved some copper sulphate crystals in a beaker of water.

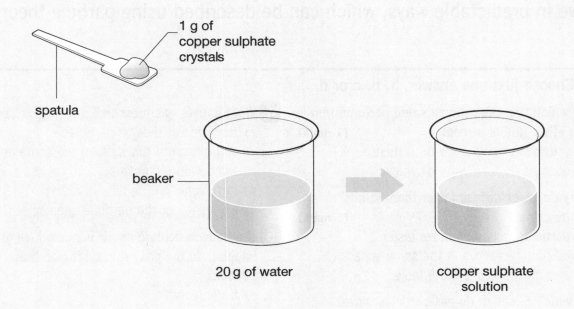

1 g of copper sulphate crystals

spatula

beaker

20 g of water

copper sulphate solution

a) What is the name of the **solvent** in Harry's experiment? (1 mark)

....

b) What is the name of the **solute** in Harry's experiment? (1 mark)

....

c) What is the mass of the copper sulphate solution that is made? (1 mark)

....

d) How would Harry know that all the copper sulphate had dissolved? (1 mark)

....

e) How could Harry make the copper sulphate dissolve more quickly? (1 mark)

....

f) Harry wants to get the copper sulphate crystals back from the solution he has made.
He places his beaker of copper sulphate solution on the windowsill of his classroom, and
waits for the water to evaporate. How could Harry make the water evaporate faster? (1 mark)

....

Score /6

How well did you do? ✗ 1–4 Try again   5–9 Getting there   10–13 Good work   14–18 Excellent! ✓

For more information on this topic, see pages 52–53 of your Success Guide.

53

Particle theory

You and everything around you are made from tiny particles. These particles behave in predictable ways, which can be described using particle theory.

A Choose just one answer, a, b, c or d.

1 By which process can you smell perfume from the other side of a room? **(1 mark)**
a) pressure
b) diffusion
c) osmosis
d) magic

2 Why do gases diffuse faster than liquids?
a) by chance **(1 mark)**
b) particles in liquids move faster
c) all particles move at the same speed
d) particles in gases move faster

3 In which direction do gas particles move?
a) upwards
b) all directions **(1 mark)**
c) downwards
d) they vibrate about fixed positions

4 What causes gas pressure? **(1 mark)**
a) the force of the gas particles colliding with the walls of the container
b) temperature changes
c) diffusion
d) expansion of the particles themselves

5 If a balloon containing air is heated, what happens to the gas pressure inside the balloon? **(1 mark)**
a) it decreases
b) it stays the same
c) the particles move more slowly
d) it increases

Score   /5

B Answer all parts of the question.

1 Complete the passage below. **(6 marks)**

In gases the .... are moving very quickly in all .... A stink bomb can be smelt from the other side of a room because of .... Scent particles from the stink bomb evaporate and turn into a .... These scent particles then bump into .... particles and are eventually spread through the whole room. People close to the stink bomb will smell it first because it takes the scent particles .... time to diffuse through the air to them.

2 Rearrange the following anagrams then draw a line to join the word you have found to its correct definition. **(5 marks)**

Anagrams		Definitions
supreres	....	One of the three states of matter. A substance in this state will fill any available space.
isfidonuf	....	To spread widely in all directions.
sag	....	A small piece of matter.
daxpen	....	A force acting on an object, equal to force divided by area.
elcartip	....	To increase in size.

Score   /11

C This is a SATs-style question. Answer all parts of the question.

1 Oliver pumps up his football.

a) Explain how the gas particles inside the football cause pressure to be exerted on the walls of the football.

(1 mark)

....

b) Oliver notices that as he pumps up his football it feels slightly warmer.

Explain how the motion of air particles changed as the football became warmer. (1 mark)

....

c) If Oliver places the football in a fridge, the air inside the ball becomes colder and the pressure inside the football changes.

i) Explain what happens to the pressure inside the football as the air particles get colder. (1 mark)

....

ii) Explain why the change in pressure occurs when the ball is cooled, in terms of the movement of air particles. (1 mark)

....

Score   /5

How well did you do?   ✗ 1–4 Try again   5–9 Getting there   10–16 Good work   17–20 Excellent! ✓

For more information on this topic, see pages 54–55 of your Success Guide.

Atoms and elements

Everything is made up of atoms. All atoms of the same element have an identical number of protons.

A Choose just one answer, a, b, c or d.

1 Which element has the symbol C? (1 mark)
a) chlorine   b) chromium
c) calcium   d) carbon

2 Roughly how many elements are there? (1 mark)
a) 100   b) 25
c) 50   d) 1000

3 Which elements are both liquids at room
temperature?   (1 mark)
a) mercury and lead
b) bromine and iodine
c) mercury and bromine
d) mercury and chromium

4 A substance is found to be made of only
one type of atom. How could it best be
described?   (1 mark)
a) an element   b) a compound
c) a mixture   d) hard

5 How are the elements arranged in the
periodic table?   (1 mark)
a) increasing mass number
b) increasing atomic number
c) colour
d) alphabetically

Score   /5

B Answer all parts of the questions.

1 Consider the following statements. Decide whether each one is true or false.

a) Most elements are metals .... (1 mark)

b) There are twenty known elements .... (1 mark)

c) Elements contain only one type atom .... (1 mark)

d) Atoms of gold are the same as atoms of oxygen .... (1 mark)

e) Compounds are formed when atoms of two or more elements are ....
   mixed together .... (1 mark)

f) Compounds are formed when atoms of two or more elements are joined together .... (1 mark)

2 Draw a line to match each diagram to its correct description.

Descriptions

a)

A mixture of two elements

b)

A compound

c)

Molecules of an element   (3 marks)

Score   /9

56

C

These are SATs-style questions. Answer all parts of the questions.

1 Read the information in the box below.

> The elements copper and iron are both shiny solids and good conductors of heat and of electricity.
>
> The elements nitrogen and oxygen are gases which do not conduct heat or electricity well.
>
> When copper is burned in air it reacts with oxygen to form a black solid called copper oxide.

Use the information in the box to answer the following questions.

a) Name an element that is a metal. (1 mark)

....

b) Name an element that is a non-metal. (1 mark)

....

c) Name a metal that can be made into steel. (1 mark)

....

d) Name a compound. (1 mark)

....

2 The symbol for the element oxygen is O.

a) How many atoms are in an oxygen molecule O_2? (1 mark)

....

Use these three diagrams to answer the questions below.

a 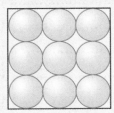   b 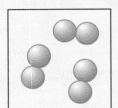   c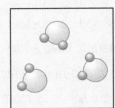

b) Which of these substances is a compound? (1 mark)

....

c) Which of these substances could be oxygen? (1 mark)

....

d) Which two substances are only made of one type of atom? (1 mark)

....

e) What is the name given to substances that only contain one type of atom? (1 mark)

....

Score /9

How well did you do? ✗ 1–4 Try again   5–9 Getting there   10–16 Good work   17–23 Excellent! ✓

For more information on this topic, see pages 56–57 of your Success Guide.

Metals

Metals are an important part of the periodic table.

A Choose just one answer, a, b, c or d.

1 Roughly three quarters of the elements in the periodic table are **(1 mark)**
a) metals
b) non-metals
c) compounds
d) atoms

2 In general, metals have: **(1 mark)**
a) high melting points and low boiling points
b) high melting points and high boiling points
c) low melting points and high boiling points
d) low melting points and low boiling points

3 Which of these is NOT a solid at room temperature? **(1 mark)**
a) calcium   b) sulphur
c) mercury   d) copper

4 What can metals be mixed together to form?
a) electricity   b) alloys   **(1 mark)**
c) sounds   d) oxides

5 Which of these metals is magnetic? **(1 mark)**
a) mercury   b) copper
c) aluminium   d) iron

Score   /5

B Answer all parts of the question.

1 Consider the following statements and decide whether each one is true or false.

a) Metals are shiny... (1 mark)
b) All metals are magnetic.. (1 mark)
c) Metals are good conductors of heat... (1 mark)
d) Metals generally have a low density... (1 mark)
e) Graphite is a non-metal which conducts electricity... (1 mark)
f) All metals are solids at room temperature. .... (1 mark)
g) There are fewer metal than non-metal elements in the periodic table. .... (1 mark)
h) Metals generally have high melting and boiling points... (1 mark)
i) All non-metal elements are gases at room temperature... (1 mark)

2 Complete the following passage. **(11 marks)**

Most of the elements in the periodic table are .... Metals generally have high melting and .... points, which means that most are .... at room temperature. The only metal that is liquid at room temperature is .... Mercury is used in .... Metals are good conductors of .... Metals have a .... appearance, particularly when the metal is freshly cut. Some metals, like iron, are .... Roughly a quarter of the elements in the periodic table are .... - .... These elements have low melting and .... points. Many of these elements are gases, a few are solids and one called .... is liquid.

Score   /20

58

C These are SATs-style questions. Answer all parts of the questions.

1 The picture below shows a saucepan. The handle is made from a different material from the rest of the saucepan.

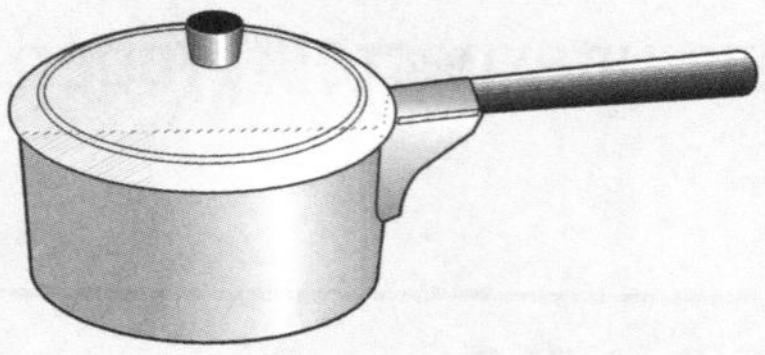

a) Use some of these words to complete the sentences below. (2 marks)

boiling point   insulator   conductor   melting point

The saucepan is made of copper. This is because copper is a good .... of heat. Copper also has a very high .... This means that copper does not melt during cooking.

b) Suggest one material that the handle of the saucepan could be made from. (1 mark)

....

c) What property of the material you have chosen as the handle for the saucepan makes it suitable for this use? (1 mark)

....

2 These statements are all true of metals.

Metals are good conductors of heat.
Metals are good conductors of electricity.
Metals are shiny.
Metals are strong.

Using only the statements listed above explain why metals are chosen for the following uses.

a) Gold is used to make necklaces. ....(1 mark

b) Copper is used to make saucepans. ....(1 ma

c) Steel is used to make bridges. ....(1 m

3 Aluminium alloys are used to make aeroplanes. Why are aluminium alloys used? Tick 2 boxes. (2

they are heavy ☐
they are strong ☐
they are light ☐
they are shiny ☐

How well did you do? 1–11 Try again 12–19 Getting there 20–27 Good work 28–34

For more information on this topic, see pages 50 & 58–59 of your Success Gui

Unusual elements

Metals and non-metals have characteristic properties. However, there are certain elements which have unexpected properties.

A Choose just one answer, a, b, c or d.

1 Which is the only non-metal element that is a liquid at room temperature? **(1 mark)**
a) mercury
b) chlorine
c) bromine
d) oxygen

2 Which is the only metal element that is NOT a solid at room temperature? **(1 mark)**
a) bromine
b) lead
c) mercury
d) tin

3 Why is mercury used in thermometers? **(1 mark)**
a) liquids expand more than solids on heating
b) solids expand more than liquids on heating
c) it is very dangerous
d) it is cheap

4 Which of these options are two forms of carbon? **(1 mark)**
a) lead and diamond
b) graphite and lead
c) diamond and gold
d) graphite and diamond

5 Why does sodium float on water? **(1 mark)**
a) sodium is reactive
b) sodium is more dense than water
c) sodium is less dense than water
d) sodium is a non-metal

Score   /5

Answer all parts of the question.

als and non-metals have characteristics.

line to connect the metals box and the non-metals box to each of its characteristic properties. two have been done for you.

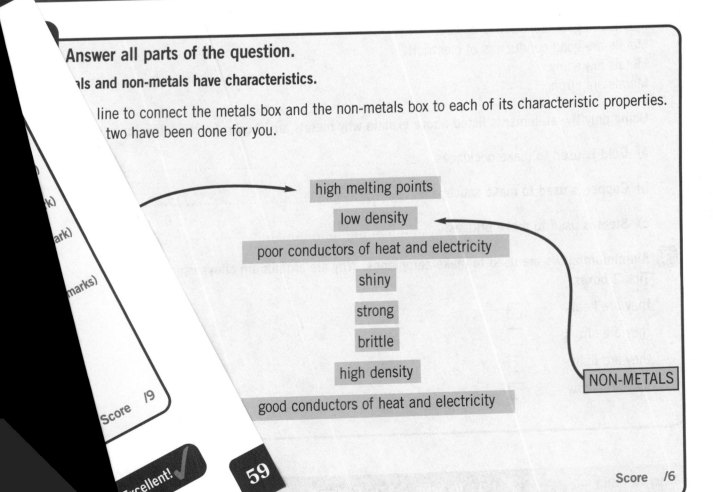

high melting points

low density

poor conductors of heat and electricity

shiny

strong

brittle

high density

good conductors of heat and electricity

NON-METALS

Score   /9

Excellent! ✓

Score   /6

C These are SATs-style questions. Answer all parts of the questions.

1 The picture below shows a saucepan. The handle is made from a different material from the rest of the saucepan.

a) Use some of these words to complete the sentences below. (2 marks)

boiling point   insulator   conductor   melting point

The saucepan is made of copper. This is because copper is a good .... of heat. Copper also has a very high .... This means that copper does not melt during cooking.

b) Suggest one material that the handle of the saucepan could be made from. (1 mark)

....

c) What property of the material you have chosen as the handle for the saucepan makes it suitable for this use? (1 mark)

....

2 These statements are all true of metals.

Metals are good conductors of heat.
Metals are good conductors of electricity.
Metals are shiny.
Metals are strong.

Using only the statements listed above explain why metals are chosen for the following uses.

a) Gold is used to make necklaces. ....(1 mark)

b) Copper is used to make saucepans. ....(1 mark)

c) Steel is used to make bridges. ....(1 mark)

3 Aluminium alloys are used to make aeroplanes. Why are aluminium alloys used?
Tick 2 boxes. (2 marks)

they are heavy   ☐

they are strong   ☐

they are light   ☐

they are shiny   ☐

Score   /9

How well did you do?   ✗ 1–11 Try again   12–19 Getting there   20–27 Good work   28–34 Excellent! ✓

For more information on this topic, see pages 50 & 58–59 of your Success Guide.

Unusual elements

Metals and non-metals have characteristic properties. However, there are certain elements which have unexpected properties.

A Choose just one answer, a, b, c or d.

1 Which is the only non-metal element that is a liquid at room temperature? **(1 mark)**
a) mercury
b) chlorine
c) bromine
d) oxygen

2 Which is the only metal element that is NOT a solid at room temperature? **(1 mark)**
a) bromine
b) lead
c) mercury
d) tin

3 Why is mercury used in thermometers? **(1 mark)**
a) liquids expand more than solids on heating
b) solids expand more than liquids on heating
c) it is very dangerous
d) it is cheap

4 Which of these options are two forms of carbon? **(1 mark)**
a) lead and diamond
b) graphite and lead
c) diamond and gold
d) graphite and diamond

5 Why does sodium float on water? **(1 mark)**
a) sodium is reactive
b) sodium is more dense than water
c) sodium is less dense than water
d) sodium is a non-metal

Score /5

B Answer all parts of the question.

1 Metals and non-metals have characteristics.

Draw a line to connect the metals box and the non-metals box to each of its characteristic properties. The first two have been done for you.

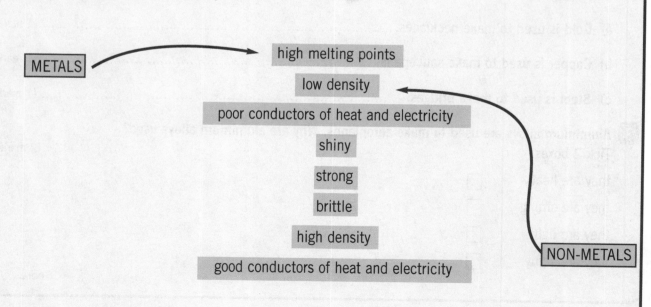

Score /6

C

This is a SATs-style question. Answer all parts of the question.

1 The diagram and table below show how four metals reacted with water.

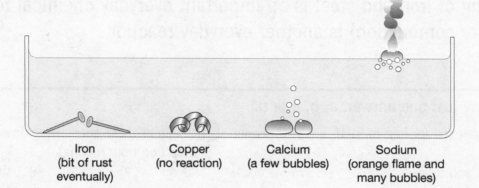

| Iron (bit of rust eventually) | Copper (no reaction) | Calcium (a few bubbles) | Sodium (orange flame and many bubbles) |

Metal	Reaction when placed in water
iron	very slowly turns brown
copper	no reaction
calcium	a few bubbles are produced
sodium	vigorous reaction, lots of bubbles are produced, sodium burns with an orange flame

a) Which metal is the most reactive?   (1 mark)

....

b) Which metal is the least reactive?`   (1 mark)

....

c) Which metal is less dense than water?   (1 mark)

....

d) What is the gas produced when the metal reacts with water?   (1 mark)

....

e) Why should sodium NOT be reacted with acids?   (1 mark)

....

Score   /5

How well did you do?   ✗ 1–3 Try again   5–7 Getting there   8–11 Good work   12–16 Excellent! ✓

For more information on this topic, see pages 58–61 of your Success Guide.

61

Chemical reactions

The rusting of iron and steel is an important everyday chemical reaction. Burning (or combustion) is another everyday reaction.

A Choose just one answer, a, b, c or d.

1 What is needed for iron to rust? **(1 mark)**
a) water
b) water and oxygen
c) water and hydrogen
d) oxygen and hydrogen

2 Rusting is an example of a chemical reaction. Describe the rate of this chemical reaction.
a) explosive
b) fast **(1 mark)**
c) very fast
d) very slow

3 Which two metals could be used to plate iron? **(1 mark)**
a) tin or chromium
b) tin or lead
c) chromium or lead
d) lead or zinc

4 Which of these substances does NOT stop iron from rusting? **(1 mark)**
a) oil
b) painting
c) plastic coating
d) water

5 Cars are made from steel. The steel is painted. In which of these situations will the steel rust? **(1 mark)**
a) when the paint is scratched
b) after 3 years
c) after 100,000 miles
d) if the car is resprayed a different colour

Score /5

B Answer all parts of all questions.

1 Which gas is required for both rusting and burning? .... (1 mark)

2 What is the name of the new substance formed when copper is burned? .... (1 mark)

3 What two substances are required for steel to rust?... (1 mark)

4 In rusting experiments:
  i) Why is calcium chloride sometimes used?.. (1 mark)
  ii) Why is the water sometimes boiled? .... (1 mark)

5 Complete the passage below. **(11 marks)**

The rusting of iron and steel is an important everyday chemical .... Unfortunately it is not a .... reaction, so we try to slow it down or stop it altogether. Steel bike chains can be protected from rusting by coating them with .... The oil prevents the oxygen and .... from reaching the steel, so rusting does not occur.

.... fences can be protected by coating them with plastic, this stops the .... and water from reaching the steel. But if the plastic is damaged the steel will ....

Another method to stop rusting is to mix iron with different metals such as chromium to form the .... stainless steel. This does not .... but steel produced in this way is more expensive to buy.

Another useful way to protect expensive .... objects is to use sacrificial ....

Score /16

C These are SATs-style questions. Answer all parts of the questions.

1 The gas used in Bunsen burners is called methane. Methane has the formula CH$_4$.

a) Give the names of the two products formed when methane is burnt. **(2 marks)**

....

b) Give the name of the gas, found in air, which is used when methane is burnt. **(1 mark)**

....

2 Sarah placed three new iron nails into test tubes. The labels on the test tubes show what was in each one.

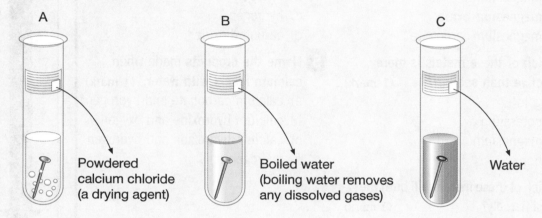

A — Powdered calcium chloride (a drying agent)

B — Boiled water (boiling water removes any dissolved gases)

C — Water

Sarah leaves the test tubes for a week.

a) After a week, in which test tube will the nail have rusted the most? **(1 mark)**

....

b) Sarah wants to use the nails to mend a fence in her garden. Suggest one way in which Sarah could stop these nails from rusting. **(1 mark)**

....

Score /5

How well did you do? ✗ 1–7 Try again 8–12 Getting there 13–19 Good work 20–26 Excellent! ✓

For more information on this topic, see pages 62–63 of your Success Guide.

63

Reactivity series

Some metals are more reactive than others. The metals can be placed in order of reactivity.

A Choose just one answer, a, b, c or d.

1 Name the compound formed when magnesium is burned. **(1 mark)**
a) calcium oxide
b) magnesium nitride
c) magnesium oxide
d) magnesium carbonate

2 Which of these metals is more reactive than sodium? **(1 mark)**
a) gold
b) potassium
c) magnesium
d) iron

3 Which of these metals will burn the most fiercely? **(1 mark)**
a) magnesium   b) zinc
c) iron   d) copper

4 Which gas is made when a metal reacts with water? **(1 mark)**
a) oxygen
b) nitrogen
c) hydrogen
d) carbon dioxide

5 Name the products made when calcium reacts with water. **(1 mark)**
a) calcium carbonate and hydrogen
b) calcium hydroxide and oxygen
c) calcium hydroxide and hydrogen
d) hydrogen only

Score /5

Most reactive
Potassium (K)
Sodium (Na)
Calcium (Ca)
Magnesium (Mg)
Zinc (Zn)
Iron (Fe)
Lead (Pb)
Copper (Cu)
Gold (Au)
Least reactive

B Answer all parts of the question.

1 Consider each of the following statements and decide whether each one is true or false.

a) Metals can be placed into an order of reactivity. .... (1 mark)

b) Gold is a very reactive metal. .... (1 mark)

c) Potassium is a very reactive metal. .... (1 mark)

d) When metals are burned in air they form metal oxides. .... (1 mark)

e) When metals are burned in air they react with the nitrogen in the air. .... (1 mark)

f) Gold does not react with dilute acids. .... (1 mark)

g) If a metal reacts with sulphuric acid the salt formed is a chloride. .... (1 mark)

h) When a metal reacts with water the gas made is hydrogen. .... (1 mark)

i) Hydrogen burns with a 'squeaky pop' .... (1 mark)

j) When zinc reacts with dilute hydrochloric acid the temperature of the acid decreases. .... (1 mark)

Score /10

KS3 Success

Workbook Answer Booklet

Science SATs

Levels 3-6

Answers

LIFE PROCESSES AND CELLS

Section A
1 b 2 a
3 d 4 c
5 d

Section B
1
movement	escaping from danger
excretion	getting rid of waste
reproduction	producing offspring
growth	reaching adult size
sensitivity	reacting to changes
nutrition	eating
respiration	releasing energy from food

2 cell membrane, cytoplasm, cell wall, chloroplasts

3 **specialised animal cells:** sperm cell, egg cell, red blood cell, nerve cell, ciliated cell, muscle cell (any two)
specialised plant cells: palisade cell, guard cell, root hair cell, xylem or phloem cells (any two)

Section C
a) (i) C (ii) B (iii) A (iv) D
b) chloroplast
c) it contains chlorophyll to absorb sunlight (accept it absorbs sunlight)
d) because it is under the ground and cannot photosynthesise (accept because it is under the ground)
e) the testes

ORGAN SYSTEMS

Section A
1 a 2 c
3 d 4 a
5 c

Section B
1 skeletal, muscle, respiratory, digestive, circulatory, reproductive, nervous, excretory, endocrine
2 A = flower B = stem
  C = root D = leaf

Section C
a) A = kidney B = bladder
b) stores urine
c) nervous system
d) skeletal, digestive, circulatory, respiratory

NUTRITION AND FOOD TESTS

Section A
1 b 2 c
3 a 4 b
5 c

Section B
1
proteins	growth and repair of cells
carbo-hydrates	for immediate energy
fibre	keeps food moving through the gut
water	allows chemical reactions to take place
fats	store of energy and insulation
vitamins and minerals	needed in small amounts to keep healthy

2 Benedict's, orange, iodine, blue/black, ethanol, cloudy white, Biuret, purple

Section C
a) carbohydrates and fats
b) vitamins or minerals or water (accept fibre)
c) cheese
d) for growth and repair of cells
e) add iodine solution (1 mark), if it contained starch the iodine would change to a blue/black colour (1 mark)

THE DIGESTIVE SYSTEM

Section A
1 b 2 a
3 a 4 c
5 b

Section B
1 (a) proteases
  (b) lipases
  (c) carbohydrases
2 (a) amino acids
  (b) fatty acids and glycerol
  (c) glucose
3 gall bladder, pancreas and liver (accept other 3 if given as an alternative answer)
4 canines, molars, premolars and incisors

Section C
1 a) we need to digest food because it is too big/large (1 mark) and does not dissolve/is insoluble (1 mark)
  b) the small intestine
  c) enzymes
  d)
Function	Organ
• removes excess water and salt from undigested food	large intestine
• adds saliva and mixes up food	mouth
• produces bile	liver
• secretes gastric juices and churns up the food	stomach

THE HEART

Section A
1 b 2 c
3 c 4 a
5 c

Section B
1 A, B, D, F, C, E
2 blood that contains oxygen
3 blood that has given up its oxygen
4 the left
5 the right

Section C
1 a) (i) C (ii) A (iii) B
  b) the capillary is the smallest blood vessel with the thinnest walls
  c) valves
  d) heart
  e) artery
  f) after exercise

BLOOD AND CIRCULATION

Section A
1 a 2 b
3 b 4 d
5 c

Section B
1 red blood cells, white blood cells, platelets, carbon dioxide, red blood cells, white blood cells, platelets, heart
2 oxygen and nutrients
3 waste products, water and carbon dioxide (any one)
4 white blood cell = A, red blood cell = B, platelets = C

Section C
1 a) white blood cells
  b) red blood cells
  c) platelets
  d) carbon dioxide and urea
  e) the red blood cell does not have a nucleus
  f) they are small and flexible (accept contain haemoglobin)

MOVEMENT

Section A
1 b 2 b
3 d 4 c
5 b

Section B
1 femur, humerus, knee cap, sternum
2 false, false, true, true, true, false
3 light; chemicals in the air; sound: chemicals in food; touch, pressure, heat and pain

Section C
1 a) line A to either muscle, line B to a tendon joining the muscle to bone
  b) they join muscle to bone
  c) (i) hip or shoulder joint
     (ii) knee, wrist joint
  d) support, protection and movement
  e) biceps and triceps

THE LUNGS AND BREATHING

Section A
1 d 2 c
3 c 4 b
5 a

Section B
1 4, 5, 1, 2, 3 (accept 4, 5, 1, 3, 2)
2 more water vapour, warmer and cleaner
3 mouth, trachea, bronchi, bronchioles, alveoli

Section C
1 a) (i) C (ii) E (iii) D (iv) A (v) B
  b) in
  c) they move down and in
  d) at the alveoli

THE MENSTRUAL CYCLE

Section A
1 a 2 c
3 b 4 b
5 d

Section B
1 **puberty** – occurs between the ages of 10 and 14 in girls and a little later in boys, a time when physical and emotional changes take place (accept examples)
menstruation – when the uterus lining and the unfertilised egg are lost each month in a period (bleed)
ovaries – where eggs are made in the female reproductive system
testes – where sperm are made in the male reproductive system
2 28 days, ovaries, day 14, ovulation, uterus lining, period, 3–7 days

Section C
a) ovaries
b) once every 28 days/once a month/every four weeks
c) the Fallopian tube/egg tube/oviduct
d) it is lost during a period/menstruation
e) testes
f) puberty
g) hormones
h) spots, hair around penis, penis gets larger, body hair on chest, start to produce sperm (accept changes related to girls)

REPRODUCTION

Section A
1 a 2 b
3 d 4 b
5 c

Section B
1 a) fertilisation
  b) implantation
2 5, 1, 2, 4, 3
3 one egg is fertilised by one sperm and divides into two

Section C
1 a) 9 months/40 weeks
  b) placenta
  c) nicotine in cigarette smoke, alcohol, drugs, etc.

(accept any named drug, accept viruses or named virus)

d) The baby receives food and oxygen by the umbilical cord through the placenta (1 mark) from the mother's blood to the baby's blood (do not accept mother's and baby's blood as implies they mix)(1 mark). Accept mother eats and breathes and this passes into the mother's blood which then diffuses into the baby's blood.

e) to protect against bumps, act as a shock absorber, cushion the foetus, support the foetus, allow the foetus to move (any one)

f) it leaves the vagina (1 mark) as afterbirth (1 mark)

DRUGS

Section A
1 b   2 a
3 d   4 c
5 a

Section B
1 alcohol, cigarette, hallucinogen, sedative, stimulant, painkiller, solvent
2 side effects are effects of the drug that are not intended such as sickness, headaches, overheating, also addiction

Section C
1 a) the risk of lung cancer gets less (1 mark) the longer a person has given up smoking (1 mark) (accept a reasonable description)
   b) (i) tar
      (ii) carbon monoxide
      (iii) nicotine
2 a) alcohol is a depressant alcohol affects the liver
   b) brain and nervous system (accept brain)

FIGHTING DISEASE

Section A
1 a   2 d
3 d   4 a
5 b

Section B
1 tick, cross, cross, tick, cross
2 fungi, virus
   bacteria, virus
   bacteria
3 the type of white blood cell that makes antibodies is the one with the large nucleus

Section C
1 a) the bacterial cell does not have a nucleus, and has a cell wall (either one)
   b) any three from broken skin, eyes, mouth, ears, nose, reproductive system
   c) white blood cells
   d) when the white blood cells produce antibodies to fight disease (1 mark) so no symptoms are felt

e) tetanus, whooping cough, food poisoning, tuberculosis, etc. (any one)

PHOTOSYNTHESIS

Section A
1 c   2 c
3 b   4 a
5 c

Section B
1 Xylem – Transport of water from the roots to the leaves. Phloem – Transport of glucose up and down the plant Stomata – Diffusion of carbon dioxide and oxygen in and out of the leaf
2 2, 4, 1, 3, 5
3 **needed** – chlorophyll, light, carbon dioxide, water
   produced – oxygen, glucose

Section C
1 a) minerals/mineral salts/nutrients (accept named mineral, do not accept food)
   b) carbon dioxide
   c) photosynthesis
   d) the leaves are the part of the plant that makes the food that a tree needs to grow/no photosynthesis can take place.
2 a) the plant under the tree did not get enough light/no sun
   b) the plant under the tree did not get enough water (accept either answer to a or b) (accept fewer minerals)

PLANT REPRODUCTION

Section A
1 b   2 d
3 c   4 c
5 a

Section B
1 M, F
   F, M
   F, F
   M, M
   F
2 correct words – stigma, self-pollination, cross-pollination, style, ovary, fertilisation, fruit, seed

Section C
1 a) the letter A should point to the ovary
   b) the letter B should point to the anther
   c) cross-pollination
   d) by the wind, by water (accept either)
   e) fertilisation
   f) wind dispersal, animals, popping out (any two)
   g) moisture

CARBON AND NITROGEN CYCLES

Section A
1 a   2 d
3 d   4 a
5 c

Section B
1 organisms that break down dead and decaying material (1 mark), bacteria and fungi are decomposers (1 mark)
2 oxygen, energy
3 fuel, water
4 they are similar (1 mark) but use different fuels (1 mark)
5 water, oxygen
6 they are the opposites of each other; photosynthesis is the reverse of respiration

Section C
1 a) 1 = photosynthesis
      2 = feeding
   b) burning/combustion
   c) it gets released into the soil (1 mark) by decomposers breaking down the bodies and waste. (1 mark)
   d) heat and pressure turn them into fossil fuels
2 a) to make proteins
   b) more nitrogen

CLASSIFICATION

Section A
1 c   2 b
3 c   4 a
5 a

Section B
1 D
2 C, D
3 A = mosses and liverworts; B = ferns; C = conifers; D = flowering plants
4 Classification

Section C
1 a) Mammal = B
      Bird = E
      Fish = A
      Amphibian = C
      Reptile = D
   b) animals with a backbone
   c) fish (accept A)
   d) amphibian (accept C)

VARIATION

Section A
1 d   2 c
3 d   4 a
5 b

Section B
1 he has the same coloured hair, eyes and big ears
2 he is tall with curly hair and freckles
3 he has inherited a combination of genes/he has inherited features from both parents
4 no
5 cloning
6 I, E
   I, E
   I

Section C
1 a) bars the correct height (1 mark)
      scale appropriate (1 mark)
      labelled axis (1 mark)
      ruler used (1 mark
   b) discontinuous variation

c) they inherit their hair colour from their parents
d) height, weight, foot size (any one)
e) the environment was different (accept examples of how the environment could have acted)

FOOD CHAINS AND WEBS

Section A
1 a   2 b
3 c   4 b
5 a

Section B
1 pyramid the correct shape, biggest bar at the bottom narrowing to the top (1 mark) bar sizes in proportion to the actual numbers (drawn to scale) (1 mark) labels added (1 mark)
2 **producer** – a plant that uses the Sun's energy to make its own food, begins a food chain
   herbivore – an animal that eats only plants
   carnivore – an animal that eats only meat.
   food chain – shows in a simple way what eats what in a community.
3 arrows pointing the correct way (1 mark) food chain in the correct order (1 mark) oak leaves ⇒ earthworm ⇒ hedgehog ⇒ fox.

Section C
1 a) rose bush
   b) ladybird and thrush (1 mark for each)
   c) the ladybirds eat the greenfly so the rose bush does not get eaten (accept there are fewer greenflies)
   d) the rest of the animals in the food chain became fewer as there was less food for them to eat
   e) the Sun
   f) food webs

ADAPTATION

Section A
1 b   2 d
3 c   4 b
5 a

Section B
1 thick fur for keeping warm blubber for keeping warm/insulation white colour for camouflage greasy fur so it does not hold water while swimming sharp claws for hunting large feet so that it does not sink in the snow (any 4)
2 a) stops other plants from growing near it so it keeps all the water and minerals/stops light reaching other plants/it is difficult to mow or pull up out of the ground (any one)
   b) so it has a better chance of growing in many places

c) difficult to pull out of the ground and so that it can reach water
d) it is quick to grow and take over the area (accept any reasonable explanations)

Section C
1 a) streamlined for swimming, fins/tail for swimming, scales for protection, it can breathe under water using gills (any 3) (do not accept it has a tail or fins or gills without qualification)
2 a) the predators eat the prey causing the numbers to decrease
b) any reasonable example e.g. cat and mouse
c) prey can run/swim/fly fast, taste horrible, camouflaged, etc. (any two)

ROCKS

Section A
1 b   2 c
3 a   4 d
5 c

Section B
1 a) true
b) true
c) false
d) false
e) true
2 a) Sedimentary rocks are softer than igneous rocks.
b) At least 50% of any limestone rock is calcium carbonate.
c) Slate is a metamorphic rock.
d) Metamorphic rocks are formed by high temperatures and pressures on existing rocks.
e) Metamorphic rocks may have bands of crystals.

Section C
1 a) The remains of dead plants and animals that have been buried for millions of years
b) sedimentary rocks
c) igneous rocks
d) X
e) sedimentary
f) metamorphic
g) P and Q will both be metamorphic rocks, but they have formed from different sedimentary rocks.

THE ROCK CYCLE

Section A
1 c   2 b
3 d   4 d
5 a

Section B
1 a) igneous, intrusive igneous, extrusive igneous, smaller
b) sediment, cemented, fossils
c) pressures, igneous, metamorphic

Section C
1 a) water
b) ice
c) water can enter the gaps, as this freezes to form ice it expands and this process can eventually break up the rock.
2 **1st event** Granite is weathered.
2nd event The weathered rock pieces are transported by rivers.
3rd event The river flows more slowly as it reaches the sea.
4th event The river deposits the sediment.
5th event Layers of sediment build up
6th event The water is squeezed out of the sediment and the rock grains become cemented together.

POLLUTION

Section A
1 a   2 c
3 a   4 b
5 d

Section B
1 fuels, sulphur, dissolves, rain, lower
2 **carbon dioxide** – greenhouse effect – ice caps may melt rise
sulphur dioxide – acid rain – damage to trees and statues

Section C
1 a) sulphur dioxide
b) many fossil fuels contain a little sulphur, when these are burnt the sulphur present can form sulphur dioxide
c) damage to trees/ buildings/ statues/ lakes, etc
2 a) carbon dioxide (accept methane)
b) ice caps melt/flooding of low level areas/disruption of normal weather patterns
3 air quality must be good.

STATES OF MATTER

Section A
1 a   2 a
3 c   4 d
5 d

Section B
1 Chlorine – gas
Bromine – liquid
Rubidium – solid
2 particles, vibrate, more/faster, more, liquid, volume, expands, solids, gas, quickly, gas

Section C
1 a) it expanded
b) it will contract
2 a) xenon
b) mercury
c) gas
d) solid
e) liquid
f) solid to liquid

DISSOLVING

Section A
1 b   2 d
3 a   4 c
5 b

Section B
1 a) true
b) false
c) false
d) true
e) true
f) true
g) true

Section C
1 a) water
b) copper sulphate
c) 21 g
d) he can no longer see the solid
e) he could warm the water, or stir it
f) open the window, or heat the solution

PARTICLE THEORY

Section A
1 b   2 d
3 b   4 a
5 d

Section B
1 particles, directions, diffusion, gas, air, less
2 **pressure** – the force acting on an object equal to force divided by area
diffusion – to spread widely in all directions
gas – one of the three states of matter, a substance in this state will fill any available space
expand – to increase in size
particle – a small piece of matter

Section C
1 a) the gas particles are moving quickly in all directions, this means that they are continually colliding with the walls of the football, causing pressure to be exerted
b) they moved faster
c) i) decreases/gets less
ii) the air particles have less energy, so move more slowly, they collide with the walls of the football less often and with less energy so the pressure decreases

ATOMS AND ELEMENTS

Section A
1 d   2 a
3 c   4 a
5 b

Section B
1 a) true   b) false
c) true   d) false
e) false   f) true
2 **diagram (a)** molecules of an element
diagram (b) a mixture of 2 elements
diagram (c) a compound

Section C
1 a) copper or iron
b) nitrogen or oxygen
c) iron
d) copper oxide
2 a) two   b) c
c) b   d) a and b
e) elements

METALS

Section A
1 a   2 b
3 c   4 b
5 d

Section B
1 a) true   b) false
c) true   d) false
e) true   f) false
g) false   h) true
i) false
2 metals, boiling, solids, mercury, thermometers, heat/electricity, shiny, magnetic, non-metals, boiling, bromine

Section C
1 a) conductor, melting point
b) wood
c) it should be a good insulator/poor conductor of heat
2 a) Metals are shiny
b) Metals are good conductors of heat.
c) Metals are strong
3 they are strong
they are light

UNUSUAL ELEMENTS

Section A
1 c   2 c
3 a   4 d
5 c

Section B
metals – shiny, strong, high density, good conductors of heat and electricity
non metals – poor conductors of heat and electricity, brittle

Section C
1 a) sodium
b) copper
c) sodium
d) hydrogen
e) sodium is too reactive

CHEMICAL REACTIONS

Section A
1 b   2 d
3 a   4 d
5 a

Section B
1 oxygen
2 copper oxide
3 water + oxygen
4 i) it removes water
ii) it removes dissolved air/oxygen from the water
5 reaction, useful, oil, water, steel, oxygen, rust, alloy, rust, steel, protection

Section C

1 a) water vapour and carbon dioxide
  b) oxygen
2 a) C
  b) paint them/grease them

REACTIVITY SERIES

Section A

1 c   2 b
3 a   4 c
5 c

Section B

1 a) true   b) false
  c) true   d) true
  e) false   f) true
  g) false   h) true
  i) true   j) false

Section C

1 a) sodium, magnesium, zinc, silver
  b) hydrogen
  c) it is too reactive
2 a) calcium or hydrogen
  b) potassium/sodium
  c) magnesium/zinc/iron/lead/copper/gold

DISPLACEMENT REACTIONS

Section A

1 d   2 a
3 a   4 b
5 c

Section B

1 i) and v)
2 a) zinc sulphate + iron
  b) iron sulphate + copper
  c) zinc sulphate + copper
  d) magnesium sulphate + copper
3 displacement, railway tracks, iron, more, displaces, oxide, heat/energy

Section C

1 a iron/copper sulphate … ✓
  copper/magnesium sulphate … ✗
  magnesium/iron sulphate … ✓
  copper/zinc sulphate … ✗
  b) magnesium, zinc, iron, copper
  c) magnesium, shinium, zinc, iron, copper
2 a) copper
  b) zinc + copper sulphate ⇒ zinc sulphate + copper
  c) copper is less reactive than magnesium

ACIDS AND ALKALIS

Section A

1 d   2 c
3 a   4 a
5 c

Section B

1 7, neutral, 1, 6, alkalis, 8, acids, alkalis, sour/bitter, indicators, colour, Indicator, acidic, alkaline, acids, orange, yellow, alkalis, purple, Alkalis, goggles

Section C

1 a) Shimmer and Shine
  b) Shine-a-Lot
  c) weakly acidic
  d) orange
  e) blue

MAKING SALTS

Section A

1 c   2 a
3 d   4 d
5 b

Section B

1 Copper carbonate is added to the acid until it stops fizzing.
The unreacted copper carbonate is then removed by filtering.
The solution is poured into an evaporating dish.
It is heated until the first crystal appears.
The solution is then left for a few days for the copper sulphate to crystallise.
2 a) true   b) false
  c) true   d) true
  e) true   f) true
3 a) hydrogen
  b) magnesium
  c) copper sulphate
  d) water + carbon dioxide
  e) water
  f) sulphuric acid

Section C

a) he could see bubbles/temperature increase
b) carbon dioxide
c) hydrochloric acid

CHEMICAL TESTS

Section A

1 b   2 d
3 a   4 b
5 b

Section B

1 carbon dioxide, bubbled, milky/cloudy, lighted, 'squeaky pop', oxygen, air, glowing, relights.
2 a) oxygen
  b) hydrogen
  c) carbon dioxide
  d) hydrogen
  e) carbon dioxide

Section C

1

Highly flammable   Corrosive

Toxic   Harmful

2 a) oxygen
  b) carbon dioxide

MIXTURES

Section A

1 d   2 a
3 c   4 a
5 c

Section B

1 **mixtures** – butter, seawater, air, granite
pure compounds – silicon dioxide, water, sodium chloride
pure elements – oxygen, neon
2 mixture, nitrogen, oxygen, element, carbon, vapour, neon, argon

Section C

1 a) neon
  b) argon
  c) gas to solid
2 a) D
  b) E
3 **compound** – calcium carbonate, copper oxide, iron sulphate
mixture – air, granite, sea water

SEPARATION TECHNIQUES

Section A

1 b   2 d
3 d   4 c
5 c

Section B

1 **salt from salty water** – evaporation
the colours in fountain pen ink – chromatography
iron from iron filings and sand – magnet
water from alcohol and water – fractional distillation
mud from muddy water – filtering
2 a) true   b) false
  c) true   d) false
  e) false   f) true
  g) true

Section C

1 a) chromatography
  b) "B" or green
  c) i) red, purple and yellow
    ii) blue and red

COMPOUNDS

Section A

1 d   2 d
3 a   4 b
5 c

Section B

1 a) false   b) true
  c) true   d) false
  e) true   f) false
  g) true   h) false
  i) true   j) false
2 atom, molecules, compound, reactions, products, reactants, iron sulphide, metal, yellow, iron sulphide

Section C

1 a) bubbles/fizzing or temperature increase or decreases in mass
  b) A gas is produced. The acid reacts with the magnesium carbonate.

NAMING COMPOUNDS

Section A

1 c   2 c
3 a   4 b
5 d

Section B

1 a) oxygen
  b) sulphur
  c) copper oxide
  d) sodium fluoride
  e) chlorine
  f) oxygen
  g) potassium iodide
  h) zinc
  i) oxygen
  j) oxygen
2 a) true   b) false
  c) false   d) true
  e) true

Section C

1 a) i) oxygen
    ii) magnesium oxide
  b) a compound, an oxide
  c) i) B
    ii) A

SYMBOLS

Section A

1 b   2 b
3 a   4 a
5 d

Section B

1 a) H   b) S
  c) N   d) Mn
  e) Cl   f) Cr
  g) Na   h) K
  i) Fe
2 a) oxygen
  b) fluorine
  c) helium
  d) bromine
  e) lithium
  f) magnesium
  g) mercury
  h) tungsten
  i) lead

Section C

1

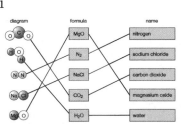

2 a) a compound
  b) **Solution** magnesium hydroxide
  Colour with U.I. blue
  Type of solution ii alkaline

SPEED

Section A

1 a   2 c
3 a   4 b
5 d

Section B

1 a) 3 b) 180 c) 10800 d) 10.8
2 a) 80 b) 800 c) 1920

3 80 km/h
4 it increases
5 it decreases
6 0 m/s   7 25 m/s
8 1000 m   9 50 s
10 the skier   11 the aircraft
12 the pilot

Section C

1 a) metre rule and timer
  b) They should measure the distance from the top of the runway to the bottom. Measure the time it takes the trolley to travel this distance. Calculate the speed of the trolley using the equation speed = distance/time. Repeat the experiment several times and take an average of their results.
  c) the greater the angle the greater the average speed
  d) 12.5 m/s
  e) make himself more streamlined, give himself a push start at the top of the ramp, etc

GRAPHS OF MOTION

Section A

1 c   2 c
3 a   4 a
5 b

Section B

1 a) BC   b) 125 s
  c) AB   d) 4 m/s
  e) 1000 m

Section C

1 a) CD   b) 0.5 h
  c) 90 km/h

2 a)

  b) 120 s   c) 80–100 s
  d) 10 s   e) 60–80 s

FORCES

Section A

1 c   2 d
3 a   4 b
5 c

Section B

1 **Balanced** These forces will have no effect on the motion of an object.
Newton This is the unit we use to measure forces.
Upthrust A force exerted upon an object placed in a liquid.
Unbalanced These forces will change the motion of an object.
Newton meter An instrument for measuring the size of a force.

Weight The gravitational force that pulls an object downwards.
Magnet This object can apply forces to other objects without being in contact.
2 a) and b)

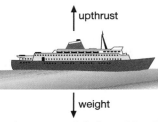

  c) they are equal d) the weight of the ship becomes greater than its upthrust.

Section C

1 a) it will extend or stretch
  b) the spring will stretch twice as much
2 a) there will be no movement as the forces are balanced
  b) the forces are unbalanced and both teams will move to the left
3 a) the ball has changed the shape of the tennis racket
  b) it may speed up, slow down or change direction

FRICTION AND TERMINAL VELOCITY

Section A

1 d   2 b
3 c   4 a
5 c

Section B

1 start, spikes, speed, streamlined, frictional, air, ice, lubricant, wax, streamlined
2 friction, lubricant, terminal velocity, air resistance, drag, streamlined

Section C

1 a) the car engine
  b) air resistance/friction between tyres and road surface
  c) i) driving force is greater than friction
     ii) driving force and friction are equal
     iii) driving force is less than friction
2 a) the surfaces of the blocks will become worn and warm
  b) axle of wheels, on chain or cogs etc

MOMENTS

Section A

1 d   2 c
3 b   4 c
5 a

Section B

1 a) no   b) yes
  c) yes   d) yes
  e) no   f) yes
  g) yes
2 a) 4 Nm   b) 20 Nm
3 a) 100 Nm   b) 75 Nm

Section C

1 a) moments
  b) the moment created by the crate is greater than the moment created by the girl
  c) move further away from the centre of the plank
  d) by moving further away from the centre of the plank she increases the moment created by her weight until it is equal to the moment created by the large crate
2 a) turn anticlockwise
  b) turn clockwise
  c) balance
  d) turn anticlockwise
  e) turn clockwise
  f) balanced

PRESSURE

Section A

1 a   2 c
3 b   4 b
5 b

Section B

1 a) false   b) true
  c) false   d) true
  e) false
2 a) 2 Pa   b) 5 Pa
  c) 10 Pa

Section C

1 a) a large force will be concentrated on a small area creating a large enough pressure to damage the floor
  b) the mats increase the area over which the force is being applied and so reduce the pressure created
  c) 400 Pa
2 a) and b)

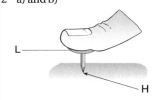

  c) Nails, spikes, knives, etc
  d) Floors and table tops, frozen lakes, handles, etc

LIGHT RAYS & REFLECTION

Section A

1 b   2 c
3 c   4 d
5 d

Section B

1 transparent, opaque, opaque, shadow, fire or star or lamp, luminous, non-luminous, light, shape, light, straight lines
2

Section C

1 a) a region of darkness where some light has been blocked off
  b) it is opaque and is blocking off light from the source
  c) the same shape as the hand
  d) light travels in straight lines
2 a) light or lamp or bulb
  b) boy, girl, door, wall, etc
  c) because she is wearing a blindfold no light can enter her eyes
  d)

REFRACTION & COLOUR

Section A

1 b   2 c
3 c   4 c
5 d

Section B

1 a) violet
  b) red
  c) red, orange, yellow, green, blue, indigo, violet
  d) they recombine to produce white light
2 a) when white light strikes the red ball, all the colours are absorbed except for red. This is reflected. So the ball looks red.
  b) when white light strikes the blue box, all the colours are absorbed except for blue. This is reflected. So the box looks blue.

Section C

1 a)

b)

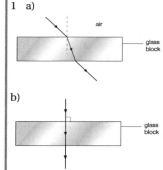

2 a) spectrum
  b) rainbow
  c) a red car
  d) a black car

SOUNDS

Section A

1 d   2 a
3 a   4 b
5 c

Section B

1 vibrating, vibrate, high, vibrate, low, hertz, 5 Hz, amplitudes, amplitudes, quiet, solids, liquids, vacuum, faster, lightning, hear

2

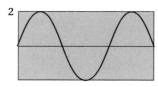

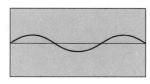

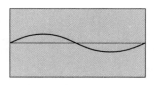

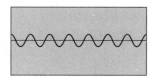

Section C
1. a) light waves travel much faster than sound waves
   b) it is reflected
2. a) the bell ringing
   b) no sound
   c) his voice causes air in his cup to vibrate. These vibrations travel along the string and make the air in her cup vibrate. These vibrations make her eardrum vibrate so she hears the sound.

ECHOES & HEARING

Section A
1. a   2. c
3. d   4. b
5. c

Section B
1. a) echoes … reflections of sound waves from surfaces
   b) sonar … use of sound waves to measure the depth of the sea
   c) ultrasound … sound of a frequency too high for us to hear
   d) hearing range … spread of frequencies that can be heard
   e) reflected … bounced off
   f) decibel scale … scale used to measure the loudness of sounds
   g) loudness … the intensity of a sound
   h) ear defenders … equipment worn by people operating noisy machinery to prevent damage to hearing
2. a) 0 dB
   b) 50-60 dB
   c) 80-100 dB
   d) 20-30 dB
   e) 120-130 dB
   f) 10-20 dB

Section C
1. a) the range of frequencies one is able to hear
   b) 19 Hz
   c) 20 100 Hz
   d) Emma
   e) ultrasound
   f) bats, dogs, dolphins
2. a) anyone operating noisy machinery, e.g. tractor driver, drill operator, etc
   b) possible permanent damage to hearing

ENERGY

Section A
1. d   2. d
3. a   4. b
5. c

Section B
1. **Gravitational potential energy** The energy an object has when it is high up.
   Sound energy Vibrating objects are sources of this energy.
   Electrical energy This energy is available every time a current flows.
   Chemical energy Food is an example of this.
   Light energy Most of your energy on Earth begins as this.
   Stored energy Forms of energy that are waiting to be used.
   Nuclear energy The energy produced by reactions in the centre of an atom.
   Kinetic energy The energy an object has because it is moving.
   Elastic potential energy Winding up a spring will give it this type of energy.
   Energy transfer When one type of energy changes into another type of energy.
2. a) Burning a candle changes chemical energy into heat and light energy.
   b) A loudspeaker changes electrical energy into sound.
   c) A battery stores chemical energy.

Section C
1. a) chemical, kinetic, heat (sound)
   b) electrical, kinetic, sound
   c) electrical, heat, light
2. a) microphone
   b) catapult or bow (and arrow)
   c) cell or battery
   d) the chemical energy in food
   e) light energy from the sun

USING ENERGY RESOURCES

Section A
1. d   2. d
3. b   4. c
5. c

Section B
1. gas, fossil, sources, plants, animals, mud, pressure, temperatures, fossil, non-renewable
2. a) **fossil fuels** fuels composed of the fossilised remains of dead plants and animals
   b) **power station** place where fuels are converted into electrical energy
   c) **acid rain** unwanted pollutant created when some fossil fuels are burned
   d) **greenhouse effect** gradual warming up of the Earth's atmosphere caused by the release of carbon dioxide when fuels are burned
   e) **pollution** material released into the atmosphere which harms the environment
   f) **renewable** can be replaced
   g) **non-renewable** cannot be replaced

Section C
1. a) coal and oil
   b) once it has been used up it can not be replaced
   c) chemical energy
   d) by burning
   e) the Sun
2. a) to heat water and change it into steam
   b) heat/thermal energy into kinetic energy
   c) kinetic energy into electrical energy
   d) drive smaller cars, use public transport more often, insulate homes, develop more efficient cars, etc

ALTERNATIVE SOURCES OF ENERGY

Section A
1. a   2. d
3. c   4. d
5. d

Section B
1. **Geothermal** – No pollution or environmental problems/Very few suitable sites
   Tidal – Reliable, two tides per day/Obstacle to water transport
   Wind – Low level technology/Possible visual and noise pollution
   Hydroelectric – Energy can be stored until required/high cost to environment i.e. flooding
   Wave – Useful for isolated islands/poor energy capture

Section C
1. a) B
   b) A
   c) C and D
   d) use alternative sources of energy, use better insulation in the home, use public transport more, etc
2. a) gravitational potential energy
   b) kinetic energy
   c) kinetic energy to electrical energy
   d) tidal and wave

HEAT TRANSFER

Section A
1. a   2. d
3. b   4. b
5. d

Section B
1. a) false   b) true
   c) false   d) true
   e) false   f) true
   g) true   h) false
   i) true   j) true
   k) true   l) false
   m) true   n) false

Section C
1. a) by conduction
   b) the wax melts and the marbles fall
   c) the first marble to fall will be attached to the best conductor
   d) saucepan
   e) saucepan handle
2. a) loft insulation (fibre glass)
   b) cavity walls or cavity wall insulation
   c) install double glazing (accept fit thick curtains)
   d) fit carpets and even better also fit underlay
   e) fit draft excluders

CIRCUIT COMPONENTS

Section A
1. b   2. c
3. a   4. a
5. a

Section B
1. charge, charges, cell, battery, wires, circuit, complete circuit, incomplete circuit

2.

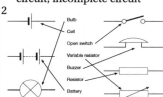

Section C
1. a) They should put their test material between the two crocodile clips. If the bulb glows the material is a conductor. If the bulb does not glow the material is an insulator.
   b) Steel … conductor, Paper … insulator, Bronze … conductor, Graphite … conductor, Mercury … conductor
   c) variable resistor
   d) bulb
   e) becomes dimmer
   f) glows more brightly
   g) no longer glows

CIRCUITS: CURRENT AND VOLTAGE

Section A
1 d   2 d
3 d   4 a
5 c

Section B
1 a) C or E
  b) E
  c) C

Section C
1 a) 1 and 2
  b) 1, 2 and 3
  c) C
2 a) 0.6 A
  b) 0.6 A
  c) 0.3 A
  d) electrical energy is changed into heat and light energy

MAGNETS & ELECTROMAGNETS

Section A
1 c   2 a
3 d   4 b
5 c

Section B
1 a) iron, steel, nickel and cobalt
  b) plastic, wood, any metal except the 4 named in part a)
  c) if suspended in the Earth's magnetic field the north pole of a bar magnet will point northwards
  d) diagram with two bar magnets with similar poles next to each other
  e)

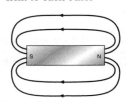

  f) the lines of force are close together where the field is strong
  g) the lines of forces are wide apart where the field is weak.

2 repel, magnet, coil, attract, core, iron, pole, electromagnet, field, compass

Section C
1 a)

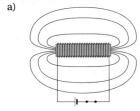

  b) more current, add more coils
  c) strength of an electromagnet can be changed (turned on and off)
2 a) the steel will be attracted to the electromagnet
  b) the aluminium will not be attracted to the electromagnet
  c) electric bell, scrapyard electromagnet

THE EARTH IN SPACE

Section A
1 a   2 b
3 a   4 a
5 a

Section B
1

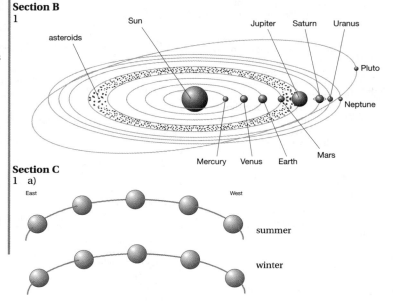

Section C
1 a)

b) because the Earth is rotating
c) 1 year
d) because the Earth's axis is tilted
e) autumn
f) summer days are warmer and daylight time is longer
2 a) Mercury, Venus
  b) closer to the Sun
  c) it will appear smaller and less bright

ACKNOWLEDGEMENTS

The author and publisher are grateful to the copyright holders for permission to use quoted materials and photographs.

Letts Educational
4 Grosvenor Place
London SW1X 7DL
School enquiries: 015395 64910
Parent & student enquiries: 01539 564913
E-mail: mail@lettsed.co.uk
Website: www.letts-educational.com

First published 2007

© Brain Arnold, Hannah Kingston and Emma Poole 2007

Design and illustration ©2007 Letts Educational Limited, a division of Huveaux Plc.

British Library Cataloguing in Publication Data. A CIP record of this book is available from the British Library.

ISBN 9781843157656

Book concept and development: Helen Jacobs, Letts and Lonsdale Publishing Director

Letts editorial team: Marion Davies and Alan Worth

Cover design: Angela English

Inside concept design: Starfish Design

Text design, layout and editorial: Servis Flimsetting

Letts and Lonsdale make every effort to ensure that all paper used in our books is made from wood pulp obtained from sustainable and well-managed forests.

C

These are SATs-style questions. Answer all parts of the questions.

1 The teacher reacted four metals with water and then with hydrochloric acid. He recorded his observations in the table below.

Metal	Observations when metal is reacted with water	Observations when metal is reacted with hydrochloric acid
silver	no reaction	no reaction
sodium	metal reacts vigorously producing bubbles of gas	too dangerous to carry out
magnesium	no reaction with cold water but steady reaction with steam	magnesium reacts quickly with acid, bubbles of gas are made as magnesium slowly dissolves
zinc	no reaction	steady reaction, bubbles of gas observed

a) Place the metals in order of reactivity.

Most reactive ....

....

....

Least reactive .... (1 mark)

b) What is the name of the gas made when magnesium reacts with hydrochloric acid?

.... (1 mark)

c) Suggest a reason why it was too dangerous for the teacher to react the metal sodium

with hydrochloric acid.. (1 mark)

2 The equation below shows the reaction between calcium and hydrochloric acid.

Calcium	+	Hydrochloric acid	→	Calcium chloride	+	Hydrogen

a) Name an element shown in the flow diagram.. (1 mark)

b) Name a metal that reacts more vigorously than calcium.................................... (1 mark)

c) Name a metal that reacts less vigorously than calcium. .... (1 mark)

Score /6

How well did you do?   ✗ 1–4 **Try again**   5–9 **Getting there**   10–16 **Good work**   17–21 **Excellent!** ✓

For more information on this topic, see pages 56–57 & 64–65 of your Success Guide.

Displacement

A more reactive metal will displace a less reactive metal from a compound.

A   Choose just one answer, a, b, c or d.

1 What happens during an exothermic reaction?
(1 mark)
a) it goes more slowly   b) heat is taken in
c) it goes faster   d) heat is given out

2 In what type of reaction does a more reactive metal take the place of a less reactive metal?
(1 mark)
a) displacement   b) neutralisation
c) oxidation   d) reduction

3 Magnesium is more reactive than copper. Magnesium is added to copper sulphate. Name the products made.   *(1 mark)*
a) magnesium sulphate + copper
b) copper oxide + magnesium
c) magnesium sulphate
d) no reaction

4 Zinc is more reactive than iron. Zinc is added to iron sulphate. Name the products made.
(1 mark)
a) no reaction
b) zinc sulphate + iron
c) iron sulphate
d) magnesium sulphate + magnesium

5 Magnesium is more reactive than iron. Magnesium is added to iron sulphate. Name the products made.   *(1 mark)*
a) magnesium oxide
b) no reaction
c) magnesium sulphate + iron
d) magnesium sulphate only

Score   /5

B   Answer all parts of all questions.

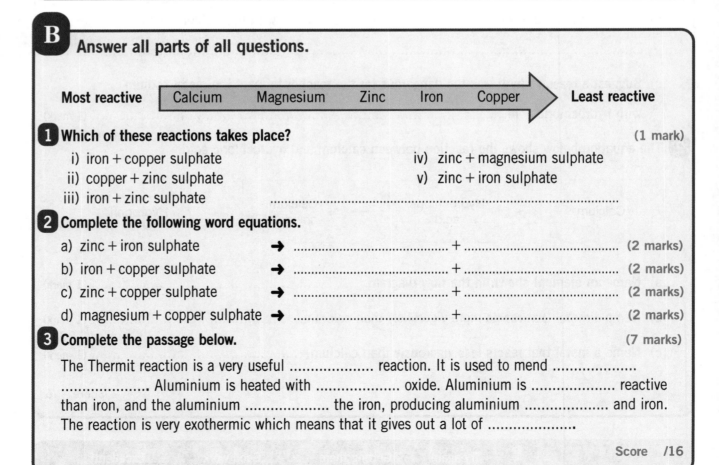

Most reactive   Calcium   Magnesium   Zinc   Iron   Copper   Least reactive

1 Which of these reactions takes place?
(1 mark)
i) iron + copper sulphate
ii) copper + zinc sulphate
iii) iron + zinc sulphate
iv) zinc + magnesium sulphate
v) zinc + iron sulphate
....

2 Complete the following word equations.
a) zinc + iron sulphate   → .... + ... *(2 marks)*
b) iron + copper sulphate   → .... + ... *(2 marks)*
c) zinc + copper sulphate   → .... + ... *(2 marks)*
d) magnesium + copper sulphate → .... + ... *(2 marks)*

3 Complete the passage below.   *(7 marks)*

The Thermit reaction is a very useful .... reaction. It is used to mend ....
.... Aluminium is heated with .... oxide. Aluminium is .... reactive
than iron, and the aluminium .... the iron, producing aluminium .... and iron.
The reaction is very exothermic which means that it gives out a lot of ....

Score   /16

C

These are SATs-style questions. Answer all parts of the questions.

1 Britney has four different metals and four different metal sulphate solutions. Britney placed a couple of drops of each solution onto a spotting tile and then added a small piece of each metal. Britney recorded her results in the table below. A tick showed that a reaction had taken place, a cross showed that no reaction had taken place.

Metal/metal sulphate solution	Copper sulphate	Magnesium sulphate	Iron sulphate	Zinc sulphate
copper	✗	....	✗	....
magnesium	✓	✗	....	✓
iron	....	✗	✗	✗
zinc	✓	✗	✓	✗

a) Complete the table to show which reactions take place. (4 marks)

b) Place the four metals in order of reactivity. (1 mark)

most reactive ...., ..., ..., ... least reactive

c) Imagine that a new metal has been discovered on another planet. It has the name shinium. Shinium displaces both copper from a solution of copper sulphate and zinc from a solution of zinc sulphate. Magnesium can displace shinium from the compound shinium oxide. Rewrite the order of reactvity to include the new metal shinium. (1 mark)

most reactive ...., ..., ..., ..., ... least reactive

2 The list below shows the names and symbols of five elements. The elements have been placed in order of reactivity.

most reactive   Potassium,   Sodium,   Magnesium,   Zinc,   Copper   **least reactive**
(K)   (Na)   (Mg)   (Zn)   (Cu)

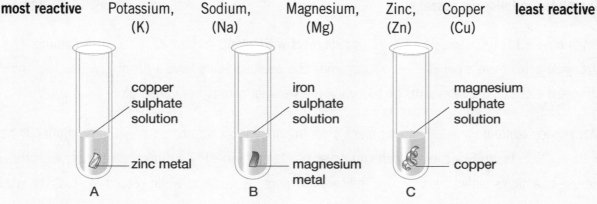

copper sulphate solution — zinc metal — A

iron sulphate solution — magnesium metal — B

magnesium sulphate solution — copper — C

In test tube A, Britney noticed that the zinc metal became covered in a brown deposit.

a) What is the name of the brown deposit? .... (1 mark)

b) Write a word equation for the reaction that takes place in test tube A. (1 mark)

....

c) Why does no reaction take place in test tube C? (1 mark)

....

Score   /9

How well did you do?   ✗ 1–7 Try again   8–13 Getting there   14–22 Good work   23–30 Excellent! ✓

For more information on this topic, see pages 66–67 of your Success Guide.

67

Acids and alkalis

Indicators are used to show whether a solution is acidic, alkaline or neutral by changing colour.

A Choose just one answer, a, b, c or d.

1 What colour is Universal Indicator in acidic solutions? **(1 mark)**
a) purple   b) green
c) blue   d) red

2 What colour is blue litmus in alkaline solutions? **(1 mark)**
a) purple   b) red
c) blue   d) green

3 What colour is red litmus in acidic solutions? **(1 mark)**
a) red   b) blue
c) green   d) orange

4 What colour is red litmus in alkaline solutions? **(1 mark)**
a) blue
b) red
c) green
d) purple

5 What is the pH of a weak acid? **(1 mark)**
a) 1
b) 7
c) 6
d) 14

Score /5

B Answer all parts of the question.

1 Complete the following passage. **(21 marks)**

Acids have a pH less than .... Acids react with alkalis to form .... solutions. The strongest acids have a pH of ...., while the weakest acids have a pH of .... The strongest .... have a pH of 14, while the weakest alkalis have a pH of ....

Many foods contain .... and many cleaning materials contain .... Acidic foods have a .... taste. However, you should never use taste to identify an unknown chemical. Instead we use chemicals called .... Indicators change .... when placed in acidic or alkaline solutions.

Universal .... is a particularly useful indicator. Not only does it show whether a solution is acidic or alkaline, but it also shows how .... or how .... the solution is. The strongest .... turn Universal Indicator red. Weaker acids like rainwater, which has a pH of around 5, turn Universal Indicator .... The weakest acids turn Universal Indicator .... Weak .... turn Universal Indicator blue, while stronger alkalis turn Universal Indicator .... are often more corrosive than acids of the same strength, so always ensure that you wear .... when using either of these two types of chemical.

Score /21

C This is a SATs-style question. Answer all parts of the question.

1 The table below shows the pH of five different shampoos.

Shampoo	pH
Shimmer and Shine	5.4
Silky	6.9
Shine-a-Lot	7.4
Healthy Hair	7.6
Super Shine	10.1

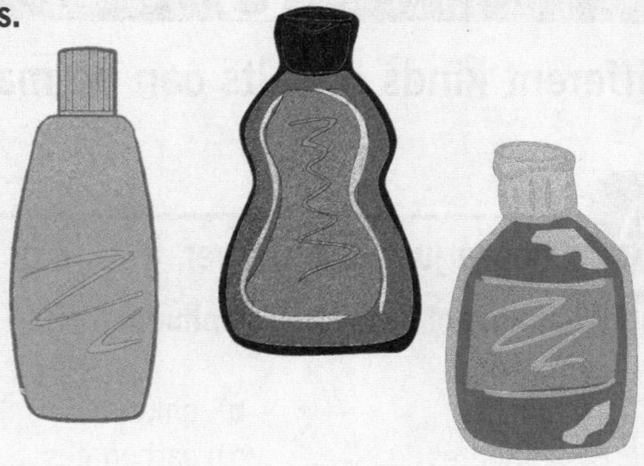

Use the table to answer the following questions.

a) Which shampoo is the strongest acid? .... (1 mark)

b) Which shampoo is the weakest alkali? .... (1 mark)

c) Tick ONE of the boxes below to show which description best describes the shampoo 'Silky'. (1 mark)

- strongly acidic ☐
- weakly acidic ☐
- neutral ☐
- weakly alkaline ☐
- strongly alkaline ☐

The table below shows the colour of Universal Indicator in different types of solution.

Description of solution	Strong acid	Weak acid	Neutral	Weak alkali	Strong alkali
Colour of Universal Indicator	red	orange	green	blue	purple

d) What colour will the shampoo 'Shimmer and Shine' turn Universal Indicator?

.... (1 mark)

e) What colour will the shampoo 'Healthy Hair' turn Universal Indicator?

.... (1 mark)

Score /5

How well did you do? 1–11 Try again 12–19 Getting there 20–26 Good work 27–31 Excellent!

For more information on this topic, see pages 68–69 of your Success Guide.

Making salts

Different kinds of salts can be made by different substances.

A Choose just one answer, a, b, c or d.

1 What kind of salts does sulphuric acid make? **(1 mark)**
a) nitrates b) chlorides
c) sulphates d) carbonates

2 What kind of salts does hydrochloric acid make? **(1 mark)**
a) chlorides b) sulphates
c) nitrates d) carbonates

3 What kind of salts does nitric acid make? **(1 mark)**
a) carbonates b) sulphates
c) chlorides d) nitrates

4 What is made when an acid reacts with a metal hydroxide? **(1 mark)**
a) salt + water + carbon dioxide
b) salt + hydrogen
c) salt + carbon dioxide
d) salt + water

5 What is made when an acid reacts with a metal? **(1 mark)**
a) salt + water
b) salt + hydrogen
c) salt + water + carbon dioxide
d) salt + carbon dioxide

Score /5

B Answer all parts of all questions.

1 The instructions below show the steps needed to make the salt copper sulphate from copper carbonate and sulphuric acid, but the order of the steps has been jumbled up. Put the sentences in the correct order to explain how the salt can be made. **(5 marks)**

a) It is heated until the first crystal appears.

b) Copper carbonate is added to the acid until it stops fizzing.

c) The solution is poured into an evaporating dish.

d) The solution is then left for a few days for the copper sulphate to crystallise.

e) The unreacted copper carbonate is then removed by filtering.

2 Consider the following statements and decide whether each one is true or false.

a) Metals react with acids to form a salt and hydrogen... (1 mark)

b) Metal hydroxides can be neutralised with water to form acids... (1 mark)

c) Metal oxides react with acids to form a salt and water. .... (1 mark)

d) Metal carbonates can be neutralised by acids. .... (1 mark)

e) Metal carbonates react with acids to form a salt and water and carbon dioxide. .... (1 mark)

f) Hydrochloric acid forms chloride salts. .... (1 mark)

3 Complete the following word equations.

a) zinc + sulphuric acid ➜ zinc sulphate + ... **(1 mark)**

b) .... + hydrochloric acid ➜ magnesium chloride + hydrogen **(1 mark)**

c) copper carbonate + sulphuric acid ➜ .... + water + carbon dioxide **(1 mark)**

B (Continued)

d) zinc carbonate + nitric acid ➜ zinc nitrate + ... + ...   (2 marks)

e) zinc oxide + nitric acid ➜ zinc nitrate + ...   (1 mark)

f) copper oxide + ... ➜ copper sulphate + water   (1 mark)

Score   /18

C

This is a SATs-style question. Answer all parts of the question.

1 In his science lesson Callum added two spatulas of zinc carbonate to 50 cm³ of sulphuric acid. A diagram of Callum's experiment is shown below.

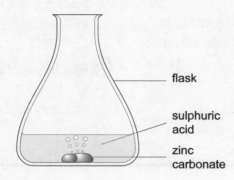

flask

sulphuric acid

zinc carbonate

a) How could Callum tell that a chemical reaction was taking place?   (1 mark)

....

The flow chart below shows the reaction that took place in Callum's experiment.

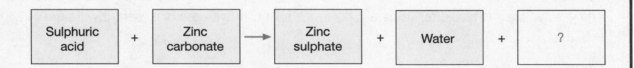

| Sulphuric acid | + | Zinc carbonate | → | Zinc sulphate | + | Water | + | ? |

b) Give the name of the other compound that was formed in Callum's experiment.   (1 mark)

....

c) Salts can also be made by reacting metal oxides with acid. Callum decides that he wants to make the salt copper chloride. He has some copper oxide. Name the acid that Callum should use to make copper chloride.   (1 mark)

....

Score   /3

How well did you do?   ✗ 1–7 Try again   8–12 Getting there   13–19 Good work   20–26 Excellent! ✓

For more information on this topic, see pages 70–71 of your Success Guide.

71

Chemical tests

Some common chemicals can be tested for using simple tests.

A Choose just one answer, a, b, c or d.

1 Which piece of apparatus would you use to measure temperature? **(1 mark)**
a) Bunsen burner
b) thermometer
c) ruler
d) measuring cylinder

2 Which piece of apparatus would you use to measure 30 cm³ of copper sulphate solution?

(1 mark)

a) ruler
b) Bunsen burner
c) thermometer
d) measuring cylinder

3 Which piece of apparatus would you use to separate a solid from a liquid? **(1 mark)**
a) filter funnel (+ paper)   b) tripod
c) clay triangle   d) gauze

4 Which piece of apparatus would you use to place 5 g of salt into a beaker? **(1 mark)**
a) spoon   b) spatula
c) fingers   d) test tube

5 Which gas relights a glowing splint? **(1 mark)**
a) hydrogen   b) oxygen
c) carbon monoxide   d) carbon dioxide

Score   /5

B Answer all parts of all questions.

1 Carbon dioxide   **(10 marks)**

Limewater is used to test for the gas .... The gas is .... through the limewater. If the limewater turns .... the gas is carbon dioxide.

Hydrogen

The gas hydrogen is tested for using a .... splint. If hydrogen is present it will burn with a ....

Oxygen

The gas .... is needed for things to burn. Things burn more brightly in pure oxygen than they do in .... If a .... splint is placed in a test tube containing oxygen, the splint ....

2 Complete these word equations

a) copper + ... ➜ copper oxide   **(1 mark)**

b) magnesium + hydrochloric acid ➜ magnesium chloride + ...   **(1 mark)**

c) copper carbonate + nitric acid ➜ copper nitrate + water + ...   **(1 mark)**

d) zinc + sulphuric acid ➜ zinc sulphate + ...   **(1 mark)**

e) zinc carbonate + sulphuric acid ➜ zinc sulphate + water + ...   **(1 mark)**

Score   /15

C

These are SATs-style questions. Answer all parts of the questions.

1 Some chemicals are dangerous and should only be used with great care. Containers holding these chemicals are marked with a label that gives information about that chemical.

Below are four hazard symbols and four hazard descriptions. Draw lines to connect each symbol to the correct description. **(4 marks)**

Hazard symbols

Description of hazard

Corrosive

Attacks and destroys living tissues including eyes and skin

Harmful

Similar to toxic, but less dangerous

Highly flammable

Catches fire easily

Toxic

Can cause death if swallowed, breathed in or absorbed through the skin

2 When toast is burnt it changes colour. Two gases are produced when toast is burnt. One of the gases is water vapour. When the other gas produced is bubbled though limewater it turns the limewater cloudy.

a) Name the gas, found in the air, which is needed for the toast to burn. **(1 mark)**

....

b) Name the gas produced when toast is burnt which turns limewater cloudy. **(1 mark)**

....

Score   /6

How well did you do?   ✗ 1–7 **Try again**   8–12 **Getting there**   13–19 **Good work**   20–26 **Excellent!** ✓

For more information on this topic, see pages 70–73 of your Success Guide.

73

Mixtures

A mixture contains two or more elements or compounds that are not joined together. Generally, mixtures are quite easy to separate.

A **Choose just one answer, a, b, c or d.**

1 Sea water is a mixture. What does it consist of?   **(1 mark)**
a) salt and gases
b) water
c) water and salt
d) water, salts and gases

2 Which of these is a mixture?   **(1 mark)**
a) air   b) copper sulphate
c) oxygen   d) quartz

Which of these is not a mixture?   **(1 mark)**
3 a) sea water
b) granite
c) calcium carbonate
d) air

4 Which of these statements is true?   **(1 mark)**
a) mixtures do not have a fixed composition
b) mixtures have a fixed composition
c) mixtures are hard to separate
d) in mixtures the atoms or compounds are joined together

5 Which of these statements is true?   **(1 mark)**
a) compounds are easy to separate
b) compounds do not have a fixed composition
c) compounds have a fixed composition
d) in compounds the atoms or particles are not joined together

Score   /5

B **Answer all parts of all questions.**

1 Consider these substances   **(9 marks)**

butter   silicon dioxide   oxygen   sea water   neon
water   air   granite   sodium chloride

Complete the table below to show whether each of these substances is a mixture, a pure compound or a pure element.

Mixtures	Pure compounds	Pure elements

2 Complete the passage below.   **(8 marks)**

Air is a .... of gases. About 78% of the air around you is .... Nitrogen is an element with the symbol N. Roughly 20% of air is .... Oxygen is also an .... and has the symbol O. Both nitrogen and oxygen occur as molecules. Nitrogen occurs as N_2 and oxygen occurs as O_2. Air also contains small amounts of other gases including .... dioxide, water .... and the noble gases .... and ....

Score   /17

C

These are SATs-style questions. Answer all parts of the questions.

1 The table below shows the melting points and boiling points of four gases.

Gas	Melting point (°C)	Boiling point (°C)
oxygen	−218	−183
nitrogen	−210	−196
argon	−189	−186
neon	−248	−246

a) Which of these gases has the lowest boiling point? .... (1 mark)

b) Which of these gases has the highest melting point?... (1 mark)

c) Oxygen is an element that can exist as a solid, a liquid or a gas. When oxygen is cooled

   from room temperature to −247°C it changes state from ....

   to .... (2 marks)

2 The diagrams below show the particle arrangements in 6 different substances.

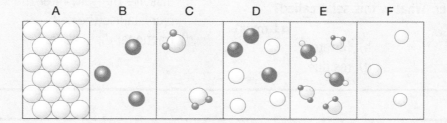

Give the letter of the diagram which best represents the arrangement of particles in:

a) a mixture of two elements... (1 mark)

b) a mixture of two compounds. .... (1 mark)

3 Consider the substances below. (6 marks)

air   granite   calcium carbonate   copper oxide   iron sulphate   sea water

Write the name of each of these substances in the correct column in the table below to show which of these substances are compounds and which are mixtures.

Compound	Mixture

Score   /12

How well did you do? ✗ 1–7 Try again   8–18 Getting there   19–28 Good work   29–34 Excellent! ✓

For more information on this topic, see pages 56–57 & 74–75 of your Success Guide.

75

Separation techniques

In a mixture the constituent parts are not joined together. Mixtures can be separated quite easily.

A Choose just one answer, a, b, c or d.

1 Which of these solids dissolves in water?
a) sand   b) salt   (1 mark)
c) chalk   d) sulphur

2 When can filtration be used?   (1 mark)
a) to crystallise salts
b) to separate two liquids
c) to separate a mixture of different coloured dyes
d) to separate a solid from a liquid

3 During filtration, an insoluble solid collects in the filter paper. What is this solid called?
          (1 mark)
a) solute   b) filtrate
c) solvent   d) residue

4 During filtration a liquid passes through the filter paper. What is this liquid called? (1 mark)
a) chalk
b) residue
c) filtrate
d) insoluble

5 Which techniques could be used to get salt from a dry mixture of salt and sand?   (1 mark)
a) chromatography
b) filter the dry mixture, crystallise the salt
c) dissolve the salt, filter the solution, recrystallise the salt
d) fractional distillation

Score   /5

B Answer all parts of all questions.

1 There are many different methods that can be used to separate mixtures. Draw a line to link each mixture to the correct technique for separating it.   (5 marks)

Mixtures	Technique
salt from salty water	magnet
the colours in fountain pen ink	fractional distillation
iron from iron filings and sand	filtering
water from alcohol and water	evaporation
mud from muddy water	chromatography

2 Consider the following statements and decide whether each one is true or false.

a) A magnet can be used to separate iron filings from a mixture of sand and iron filings. .... (1 mark)
b) Filtering can be used to separate salt from salty water. .... (1 mark)
c) Filtration can be used to separate an insoluble solid from a liquid. .... (1 mark)
d) During filtration the solid which remains in the filter paper is called the filtrate. .... (1 mark)
e) Salt is insoluble in water. .... (1 mark)
f) Sand can be separated from a mixture of salt and sand by dissolving the salt in water and then filtering the mixture. .... (1 mark)
g) Chromatography can be used to separate mixtures of the different coloured dyes in orange food colouring. .... (1 mark)

Score   /12

C This is a SATs-style question. Answer all parts of the question.

1 Karl has two black felt tip pens. He labels them A and B.

Karl wants to identify the different coloured inks found in each of his pens and carries out the experiment shown below.

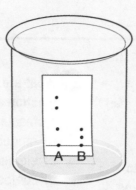

a) What is the name given to this method of separating mixtures of different coloured

   dyes? .... (1 mark)

Karl then repeated the experiment using his other coloured felt tip pens.

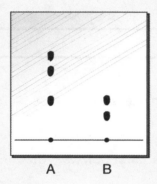 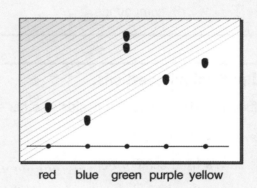

A	B

red   blue   green   purple   yellow

b) Use Karl's results to identify a felt tip pen whose ink is made of two coloured dyes.   (1 mark)

   ....

c) i) Identify the three coloured dyes in black felt tip pen A. .... (1 mark)

   ii) Identify the two coloured dyes in black felt tip pen B.. (1 mark)

Score   /4

How well did you do?   ✗ 1–4 Try again   5–8 Getting there   9–15 Good work   16–21 Excellent! ✓

For more information on this topic, see pages 76–77 of your Success Guide.

77

Compounds

If atoms of two or more elements are joined together they form a compound. Compounds have a fixed composition.

A Choose just one answer, a, b, c or d.

1 If you saw bubbles being given off during a reaction, what is being made? **(1 mark)**
a) a solution   b) a liquid
c) a solid   d) a gas

2 Which piece of apparatus would you use to find if the temperature had increased during a reaction? **(1 mark)**
a) mass balance   b) Bunsen burner
c) measuring cylinder   d) thermometer

3 What are the chemicals at the start of a reaction always called? **(1 mark)**
a) reactants   b) products
c) elements   d) compounds

4 What are the chemicals at the end of a reaction always called? **(1 mark)**
a) reactants
b) products
c) elements
d) compounds

5 If iron is heated with sulphur what is formed? **(1 mark)**
a) iron sulphur
b) iron oxide
c) iron sulphide
d) iron sulphate

Score   /5

B Answer all parts of all questions.

1 Consider the following statements and decide whether each one is true or false.

a) Mixtures have a fixed composition. ....(1 mark)

b) Compounds have a fixed composition. ....(1 mark)

c) New substances are made during a chemical reaction. ....(1 mark)

d) New substances made in a chemical reaction are called reactants. ....(1 mark)

e) Iron is magnetic. ....(1 mark)

f) Iron sulphide is magnetic. ....(1 mark)

g) If atoms of two or more elements are joined together a compound is formed. ....(1 mark)

h) A gas is always given off during a chemical reaction. ....(1 mark)

i) If bubbles are produced during a chemical reaction, this shows that a gas is being made.

   ....(1 mark)

j) During most chemical reactions the temperature decreases slightly. ....(1 mark)

2 Complete the passage below. **(10 marks)**

Elements are made of only one type of .... If atoms of the same elements are joined

together they form .... of the element. The oxygen and nitrogen in the air around us are in

the form of molecules.

B (Continued)

If the atoms of two (or more) different elements are chemically joined together they form molecules of a .... New substances are formed by chemical .... These new substances are called the .... The products of a chemical reaction can have very different properties from the .... at the start of the reaction. When iron and sulphur are heated together they can form a new substance called .... Iron is a magnetic .... Sulphur is a .... solid. But, ... has very different properties from both iron and sulphur. It is a non-magnetic black solid.

Score   /20

C

This is a SATs-style question. Answer all parts of the question.

1 Eric placed a flask containing 75 cm³ of acid on a balance. He added 5 g of magnesium carbonate.

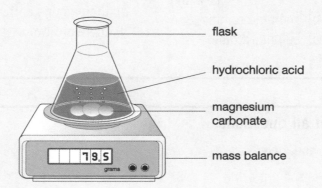

flask

hydrochloric acid

magnesium carbonate

mass balance

79.5 grams

a) How could Eric tell that a chemical reaction was taking place?   (1 mark)

....

b) Look at Eric's experiment. Which of these statements is true? Tick two boxes.   (2 marks)

Magnesium carbonate does not react.   ☐

A gas is produced.   ☐

The acid reacts with the magnesium carbonate.   ☐

The hydrochloric acid is boiling.   ☐

The acid can be burnt to release energy in the form of heat.   ☐

The hydrochloric acid in the experiment is a gas.   ☐

Score   /3

How well did you do?   ✗ 1–7 Try again   8–14 Getting there   15–21 Good work   22–28 Excellent! ✓

For more information on this topic, see pages 56–57 & 78–79 of your Success Guide.

Naming compounds

When atoms of two or more elements join together they form a compound. Compounds are generally difficult to separate.

A

Choose just one answer, a, b, c or d.

1 What is the name of the compound $CuSO_4$? (1 mark)

a) copper sulphur b) calcium sulphate
c) copper sulphate d) calcium sulphide

2 What is the name of the compound MgO?

a) manganese oxide b) magnesium oxygen
c) magnesium oxide d) magnesium sulphate

(1 mark)

3 What is the name of the compound NaBr? (1 mark)

a) sodium bromide b) sodium bromine
c) sodium chloride d) sulphur bromide

4 What is the name of the compound KI? (1 mark)

a) potassium bromide
b) potassium iodide
c) potassium chloride
d) sodium iodide

5 What does the 'di' in carbon dioxide show? (1 mark)

a) there are two carbon atoms
b) there is one oxygen atom
c) there is one carbon atom
d) there are two oxygen atoms

Score /5

B

Answer all parts of all questions.

1 Complete the following equations.

a) sodium + ... ➔ sodium oxide (1 mark)
b) iron + ... ➔ iron sulphide (1 mark)
c) copper + oxygen ➔ .... (1 mark)
d) sodium + fluorine ➔ .... (1 mark)
e) sodium + ... ➔ sodium chloride (1 mark)
f) magnesium + ... ➔ magnesium oxide (1 mark)
g) potassium + iodine ➔ .... (1 mark)
h) .... + oxygen ➔ zinc oxide (1 mark)
i) .... + hydrogen ➔ water (1 mark)
j) carbon + ... ➔ carbon dioxide (1 mark)

2 Consider the following the statements and decide whether each one is true or false.

a) Magnesium iodide is a compound ....(1 mark)
b) Compounds are usually easy to separate ....(1 mark)
c) Water is a compound formed from two elements hydrogen and carbon ....(1 mark)
d) If aluminium reacts with oxygen it forms a compound called aluminium oxide....................(1 mark)
e) When sodium reacts with bromine it forms a compound called sodium bromide ....(1 mark)

Score /15

C This is a SATs-style question. Answer all parts of the question.

1 In her science lesson Tanya heated some magnesium ribbon. The magnesium burnt fiercely and Tanya was left with a white powder.

a) i) Name the gas in the air which reacted with magnesium in Tanya's experiment.

.... (1 mark)

ii) Name the white powder that Tanya has made. .... (1 mark)

b) What type of substance was the white powder that Tanya has made? Tick two boxes.

(2 marks)

An element ☐

A compound ☐

A carbonate ☐

An oxide ☐

A chloride ☐

c) The diagrams below show the arrangement of particles in three different substances.

A   B   C

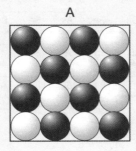   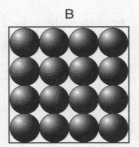   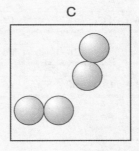

Which of the diagrams best represents the arrangement of particles

i) in the magnesium ribbon in Tanya's experiment? .... (1 mark)

ii) in the white ash that Tanya made? .... (1 mark)

Score   /6

Symbols

In science, elements and compounds can be represented by simple symbols.

A Choose just one answer, a, b, c or d.

1 The symbol for magnesium is: (1 mark)
   a) mg   b) Mg
   c) M   d) MG

2 The symbol for sodium is: (1 mark)
   a) S   b) Na
   c) So   d) NA

3 Look at the formula for calcium carbonate, $CaCO_3$. How many carbon atoms are present?   (1 mark)
   a) 1   b) 2
   c) 3   d) 4

4 Look at the formula for carbon dioxide, CO_2. How many oxygen atoms are present?   (1 mark)
   a) 2   b) 1   c) 3   d) 4

5 Which of these statements is true?   (1 mark)
   a) If a gas is made in a reaction it will have no mass.
   b) In chemical reactions, the reactants will have a greater mass than the products.
   c) In chemical reactions, the products will have a greater mass than the reactants.
   d) In chemical reactions, the overall mass before and after is the same.

Score   /5

B Answer all parts of all questions.

H Hydrogen																	
Li Lithium	Be Beryllium											B Boron	C Carbon	N Nitrogen	O Oxygen	F Fluorine	Ne Neon
Na Sodium	Mg Magnesium											Al Aluminium	Si Silicon	P Phophorus	S Sulphur	Cl Chlorine	Ar Argon
K Potassium	Ca Calcium	Sc Scandium	Ti Titanium	V Vanadium	Cr Chromium	Mn Manganese	Fe Iron	Co Cobalt	Ni Nickel	Cu Copper	Zn Zinc	Ga Gallium	Ge Germanium	As Arsenic	Se Selenium	Br Bromine	Kr Krypton
Rb Rubidium	Sr Strontium	Y Yttrium	Zr Zirconium	Nb Niobium	Mo Molydendum	Tc Technetium	Ru Ruthenium	Rh Rhodium	Pd Palladium	Ag Silver	Cd Cadmium	In Indium	Sn Tin	Sb Antimony	Te Tellurium	I Iodine	Xe Xenon
Cs Caesium	Ba Barium	La Lanthanum	Hf Hafnium	Ta Tantalum	W Tungsten	Re Rhenium	Os Osmium	Ir Iridium	Pt Platinum	Au Gold	Hg Mercury	Tl Thallium	Pb Lead	Bi Bismuth	Po Polonium	At Astatine	Rn Radon
Fr Francium	Ra Radium	Ac Actinium															

He Helium

1 Find the symbol for the following elements: (9 marks)

   a) hydrogen   b) sulphur   c) nitrogen   d) manganese   e) chlorine   f) chromium

   g) sodium   h) potassium   i) iron

2 Find the name of the elements whose symbols are listed below: (9 marks)

   a) O   b) F   c) He   d) Br   e) Li   f) Mg   g) Hg   h) W   i) Pb

Score   /18

C

These are SATs-style questions. Answer all parts of the questions.

1 Look at the diagrams below. In the diagrams each circle represents one atom. Draw a line to join each diagram to the correct name and the correct formula. The first one is done for you. **(4 marks)**

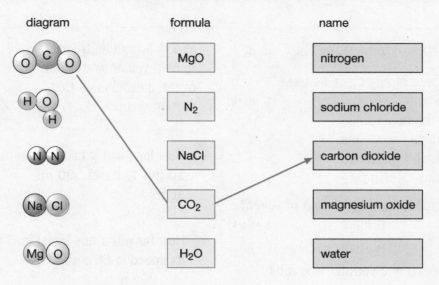

diagram   formula   name

	MgO	nitrogen
	N₂	sodium chloride
	NaCl	carbon dioxide
	CO₂	magnesium oxide
	H₂O	water

2 At school Sam burnt some magnesium ribbon. The name of the white ash formed when magnesium is burnt is magnesium oxide.

a) What type of substance is magnesium oxide? Tick one box. **(1 mark)**

an element ☐

a mixture ☐

a compound ☐

a carbonate ☐

b) The white ash is sparingly soluble in water. Sam dissolves some of the white ash she has made in a beaker of water to form a magnesium hydroxide solution.

Sam then tests the solution using Universal Indicator paper. The magnesium hydroxide solution has a pH of 8. Complete the table below to show:

i) The colour of the Universal Indicator paper in this solution **(1 mark)**

ii) The type of solution: acidic/neutral/alkaline **(1 mark)**

Solution	Colour with Universal Indicator	Type of solution
magnesium hydroxide		

Score /7

How well did you do? ✗ 1–7 Try again   8–13 Getting there   14–22 Good work   23–30 Excellent! ✓

For more information on this topic, see pages 68, 80 & 82–83 of your Success Guide.

Speed

The speed of an object tells us how fast it is moving.

A Choose just one answer, a, b, c or d.

Use this formula triangle to help you answer some of the questions on this section of work.

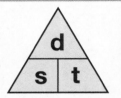

1 To find the speed of an object we use the equation: **(1 mark)**
   a) Speed = distance / time.
   b) Speed = distance × time
   c) Speed = time / distance
   d) Speed = time × distance

2 **Which of the following is not a unit of speed?**
   a) m/s   b) km/h   **(1 mark)**
   c) m   d) cm/s

3 **What is the speed of a sprinter who runs 160 m in 20 s?**   **(1 mark)**
   a) 8 m/s   b) 0.8 m/s
   c) 320 m/s   d) 32 m/s

4 **How long will it take a man running at 10 m/s to travel 500 m?**   **(1 mark)**
   a) 5 s   b) 50 s
   c) 5000 s   d) 0.5 h

5 **How far will a bus travel in 5 hours if its speed is 60 km/h?**   **(1 mark)**
   a) 120 km
   b) 12 km
   c) 24 km
   d) 300 km

Score   /5

B Answer all parts of the questions. Show all your workings for numerical questions.

1 A pupil walking at 3 m/s will travel a) .... m every second. In one minute she will walk b) .... m. In one hour she will walk c) .... m or d) .... km.   **(4 marks)**

2 A car travelling at 80 km/h will travel a) .... km every hour. In 10 hours it will have travelled b) .... km and in one full day it will have travelled c) .... km.   **(3 marks)**

3 What is the speed of a train that travels 240 km in 3 hours?   **(1 mark)**

4 What happens to the speed of a bus if it is accelerating?   **(1 mark)**

5 What happens to the speed of a train if it is decelerating?   **(1 mark)**

6 What is the speed of an object which is 'stationary'?   **(1 mark)**

7 Calculate the speed of a car that travels 500 m in 20 s.   **(1 mark)**

8 Calculate the distance travelled by a pupil who cycles at 25 m/s for 40 s.   **(1 mark)**

9 Calculate the time it takes a jogger to run 200 m whilst jogging at a speed of 4 m/s.   **(1 mark)**

10 Which is travelling faster, a cyclist who travels 400 m in 20 s or a skier who travels 1500 m in 1 min?   **(1 mark)**

11 Which will travel further, a woman who runs at 5 m/s for 1 hour or an aircraft that travels at 180 m/s for 2 mins?   **(1 mark)**

12 Whose journey takes the longer, a driver travelling a distance of 400 km at an average speed of 80 km/h or a pilot travelling a distance of 8,000 km at an average speed of 1500 km/h?   **(1 mark)**

Score   /17

C   This is a SATs-style question. Answer all parts of the question.

1 Katy and Richard are carrying out an experiment to discover the average speed of a trolley as it travels down their runway.

a) What two pieces of apparatus not shown in the above diagram will the two pupils need to carry out their investigation?   (2 marks)

....

....

b) Explain in your own words what Katy and Richard should do with the apparatus and what measurements they should make to find the average speed of the trolley as it travels down the runway.   (4 marks)

....

....

....

c) What effect do you think increasing the angle of the runway will have on the average speed of the trolley?   (1 mark)

....

....

d) A skier takes 4 s to travel down a slope 50 m long. Calculate the average speed of the skier on the slope.   (3 marks)

....

....

e) Suggest one way in which the skier could increase his average speed down the slope.   (1 mark)

....

....

Score   /11

Graphs of motion

It is often useful to show the motion of an object in the form of a graph. There are two types of graph you should be familiar with: distance–time graphs and speed– or velocity–time graphs.

A Choose just one answer, a, b, c or d.

1 A horizontal line on a distance–time graph tells us that the object is: (1 mark)
   a) travelling up a steep hill
   b) travelling at a high constant speed
   c) stationary
   d) decelerating

2 A sloping straight line on a distance–time graph tells us that the object is: (1 mark)
   a) decelerating
   b) accelerating
   c) moving at a constant speed
   d) going up hill

3 A horizontal line on a speed–time graph tells us that the object is: (1 mark)
   a) travelling at a constant speed
   b) going uphill
   c) accelerating
   d) stationary

4 A line which is sloping upwards on a speed–time graph tells us that the object is: (1 mark)
   a) accelerating
   b) travelling at a constant speed
   c) going uphill
   d) stationary

5 A line which is sloping downwards on a speed–time graph tells us that the object is: (1 mark)
   a) travelling at a constant speed
   b) decelerating
   c) going downhill
   d) stationary

Score   /5

B Answer all parts of all questions. Show all your workings for numerical questions.

1 The distance–time graph below shows the journey of a walker.

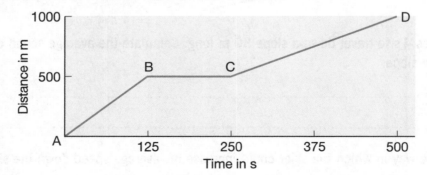

a) During which part of the journey was the walker stationary?   (1 mark)
b) For how long was the walker stationary?   (1 mark)
c) During which part of the journey was the walker moving fastest?   (1 mark)
d) Calculate the fastest speed of the walker.   (1 mark)
e) What is the total distance travelled by the walker?   (1 mark)

Score   /5

These are SATs-style questions. Answer all parts of the questions.

1 The speed–time graph for a
car journey is shown opposite.

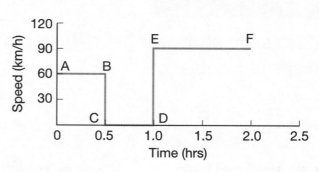

a) During which part of the journey was the car stationary? (1 mark)

b) For how long was the car stationary? (1 mark)

c) What was the fastest speed of the car? (1 mark)

2 Katy went for a very short journey in her dad's car. She noted down the speed of the car every 10
seconds. Her results are shown in the table below.

Time in seconds	0	10	20	30	40	50	60	70	80	90	100	110	120
Speed of car in km/h	0	20	40	60	30	0	0	40	80	80	80	0	0

a) Draw a speed–time graph for Katy's journey. (6 marks)

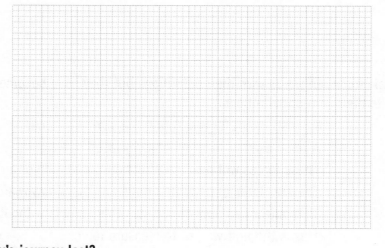

b) How long did Katy's journey last? (1 mark)

....

c) Between which two readings was she travelling fastest? (1 mark)

....

d) For how long was Katy stationary in the middle of her journey? (1 mark)

....

e) During which part of the journey did Katy's car have the greatest acceleration? (1 mark)

....

Score /13

GRAPHS OF MOTION

Physics

Forces

Most forces are pushes or pulls. They can affect the motion and shape of an object.

A Choose just one answer, a, b, c or d.

1 We measure forces using: **(1 mark)**
   a) ammeter   b) voltmeter
   c) Newton meter   d) joulemeter

2 We measure the size of a force in units called:
   a) amperes   b) volts **(1 mark)**
   c) joules   d) newtons

3 Which of the following may happen if balanced forces are applied to an object? **(1 mark)**
   a) it will travel at a constant speed
   b) it will accelerate
   c) it will decelerate
   d) it will change direction

4 Which of the following is not an example of balanced forces? **(1 mark)**
   a) a box on a table
   b) a car accelerating
   c) a cork floating on water
   d) a weight hanging from a spring

5 The force exerted on an object by gravity is called the object's: **(1 mark)**
   a) mass
   b) density
   c) weight
   d) viscosity

Score /5

B Answer all parts of all questions.

1 The two lists below contain words with their definitions but they have become muddled. Join the words to their correct definitions. **(7 marks)**

balanced	An instrument for measuring the size of a force.
Newton	A force exerted upon an object placed in a liquid.
upthrust	These forces will have no effect on the motion of an object.
unbalanced	The gravitational force that pulls an object downwards.
Newton meter	This object can apply forces to other objects without being in contact.
weight	This is the unit we use to measure forces.
magnet	These forces will change the motion of an object.

2 The diagram opposite shows a ship floating on water.

a) Add one arrow to the diagram to show the weight of the ship. Label this arrow 'weight'. **(1 mark)**

b) Add a second arrow to the diagram to show the upthrust from the water on the ship. Label this arrow 'upthrust'. **(1 mark)**

c) If the ship is floating write one sentence that compares the sizes of these two forces. **(1 mark)**

....

d) Explain why a ship which fills with water sinks. **(1 mark)**

....

Score /11

C

These are SATs-style questions. Answer all parts of the questions.

1 The diagram opposite shows a spring attached to a stand.

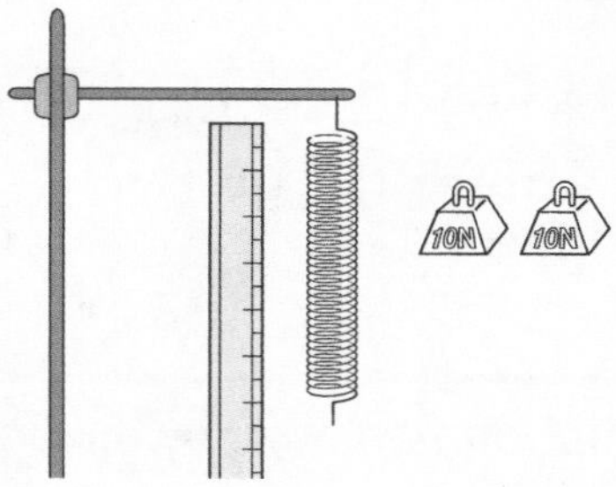

a) What will happen to the spring if a 10 N weight is hung on the end of it? (1 mark)

....

b) What will happen to the spring if a second 10 N weight is added to the spring? (1 mark)

....

2 The cartoon opposite shows two tug of war teams.

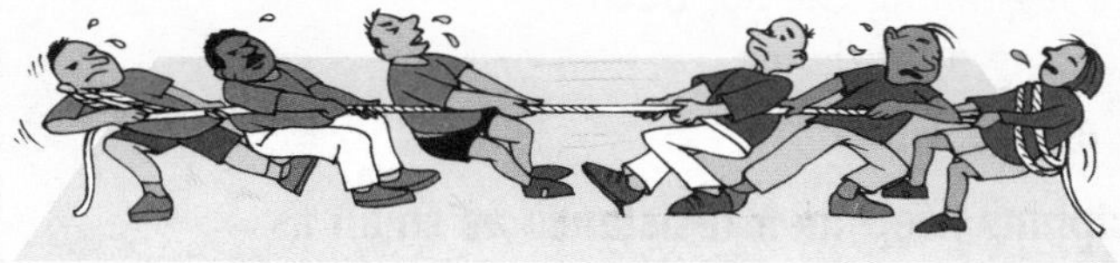

a) Explain what will happen if both teams pull with the same force. (1 mark)

....

b) Explain what will happen if the team on the left pulls with a greater force than the team on the right. (1 mark)

....

3 The cartoon opposite shows a tennis ball hitting a racket.

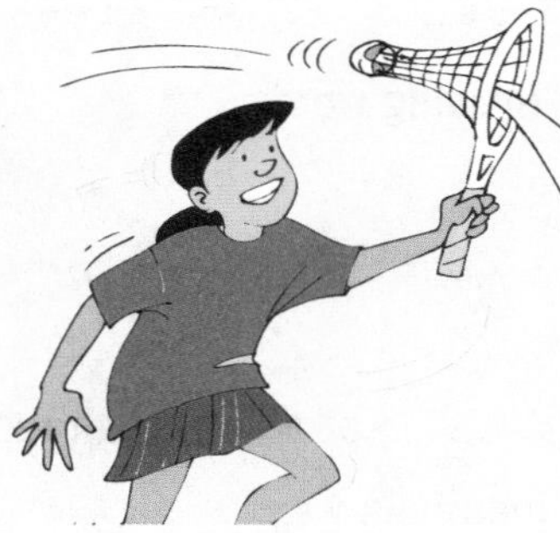

a) Explain how we know from the cartoon that the ball is applying a force to the racket. (1 mark)

....

b) Suggest three ways in which the motion of the tennis ball may change as it is struck by the racket. (3 marks)

....

....

....

Score /8

How well did you do? 1–4 Try again 5–9 Getting there 10–16 Good work 17–24 Excellent!

For more help on this topic see KS3 Science Success Guide pages 90–91

Friction and terminal velocity

Whenever an object moves or tries to move, a force will oppose it.
This force is called friction.

A Choose just one answer, a, b, c or d.

1 A force which opposes motion is: (1 mark)
   a) mass   b) weight
   c) viscosity   d) friction

2 Friction between surfaces can be increased by:
   a) polishing the surfaces   (1 mark)
   b) roughening the surfaces
   c) using a lubricant
   d) adding water

3 Dolphins keep their resistance as small as
   possible by: (1 mark)
   a) swimming under water
   b) being mammals
   c) having a streamlined shape
   d) being fish

4 Another name for air resistance is: (1 mark)
   a) drag
   b) upthrust
   c) weight
   d) mass

5 As the speed of an object moving through air
   increases the frictional forces: (1 mark)
   a) decrease
   b) stay the same
   c) increase
   d) act in the direction of the motion

Score   /5

B Answer all parts of all questions.

1 Fill in the missing words.   (10 marks)

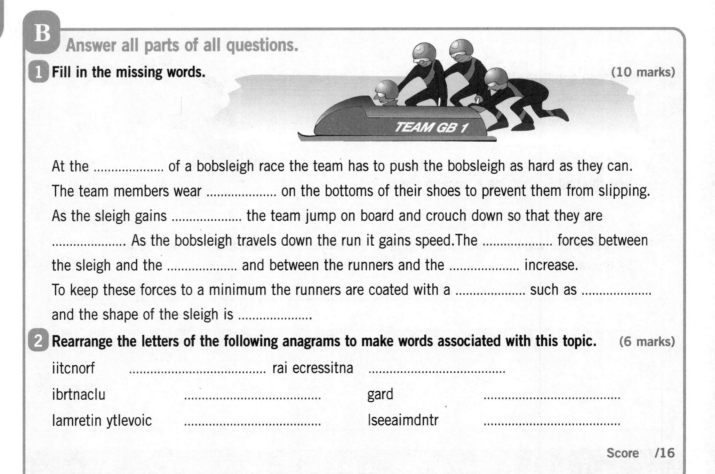

TEAM GB 1

At the .... of a bobsleigh race the team has to push the bobsleigh as hard as they can.

The team members wear .... on the bottoms of their shoes to prevent them from slipping.

As the sleigh gains .... the team jump on board and crouch down so that they are

.... As the bobsleigh travels down the run it gains speed. The .... forces between

the sleigh and the .... and between the runners and the .... increase.

To keep these forces to a minimum the runners are coated with a .... such as ....

and the shape of the sleigh is ....

2 Rearrange the letters of the following anagrams to make words associated with this topic.   (6 marks)

iitcnorf   .... rai ecressitna   ....

ibrtnaclu   .... gard   ....

lamretin ytlevoic .... lseeaimdntr   ....

Score   /16

C

1 The diagram below shows the forces acting on a car travelling along a flat road.

driving force   friction

a) **What provides the driving force for the car?** (1 mark)

....

b) **Give one source of the frictional forces acting upon the car.** (1 mark)

....

....

c) **Compare the sizes of the driving force and the frictional forces** (3 marks)

  i)   when the car is accelerating

     ....

  ii) when the car is travelling at a constant speed

     ....

  iii) when the car is decelerating

     ....

2 The diagram opposite shows the brake blocks on a bicycle.

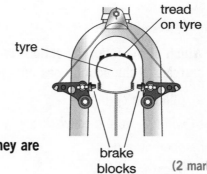

tread on tyre

tyre

brake blocks

a) **Name two things that will happen to the brake blocks when they are used to slow the bicycle.** (2 marks)

....

....

b) **Name one place on a bicycle where oil is used as a lubricant.** (1 mark)

....

Score   /8

Moments

Forces sometimes make objects turn or rotate. The turning effect of a force is called a moment.

A Choose just one answer, a, b, c or d.

1 A moment is: (1 mark)
- a) the size of a force
- b) the stretching effect of a force
- c) the squashing effect of a force
- d) the turning effect of a force

2 Which of the following will not affect the size of the moment applied by a spanner? (1 mark)
- a) the length of the spanner
- b) the size of the force
- c) the size of the nut
- d) the distance between the nut and the point where the force is applied

3 Calculate the moment created when a force of 100 N is applied by a spanner which is 0.4 m long. (1 mark)
- a) 400 Nm
- b) 40 Nm
- c) 25 Nm
- d) 250 Nm

4 If the clockwise moments applied to an object are equal to the anticlockwise moments, the object will: (1 mark)
- a) turn to the left
- b) turn to the right
- c) not turn
- d) turn clockwise

5 A girl weighing 500 N sits 1.5 m from the centre of a see-saw. Her friend weighs 750 N. How far should she sit from the centre of the see-saw if it is to balance? (1 mark)
- a) 1 m
- b) 2 m
- c) 1.5 m
- d) 0.75 m

Score   /5

B Answer all parts of all questions. Show all your working for numerical questions.

1 Which of the following actions creates a moment? Write 'Yes' if the action creates a moment, and 'No' if the action does not create a moment. (7 marks)

- a) pulling a spring ....
- b) winding up a clockwork toy ....
- c) opening a door ....
- d) opening a book ....
- e) pressing a drawing pin into a board ....
- f) turning on a water tap ....
- g) passing through a turnstile ....

2 a) Calculate the size of the moment created by a spanner 0.4 m long when a force of 10 N is applied to it. (1 mark)

b) Calculate the size of the moment created by a spanner 0.4 m long when a force of 50 N is applied to it. (1 mark)

F

pivot

0.4m

B (Continued)

3 a) Calculate the size of the moment created when a force of 50 N is applied to a lever 2.0 m long. **(1 mark)**

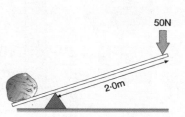

b) Calculate the size of the moment created when a force of 50 N is applied to a lever 1.5 m long. **(1 mark)**

Score /11

C

These are SATs-style questions. Answer all parts of the questions.

1 The picture opposite shows a girl sitting on one end of a plank of wood that has a large crate on the other end.

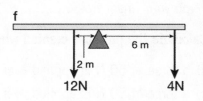

a) What are both the weight of the girl and the weight of the crate creating? **(1 mark)**

....

b) Why is the plank tilted? **(1 mark)**

....

c) Explain what the girl should do in order to make the plank balance. **(1 mark)**

....

d) Explain why the action you have described in part c) will balance the plank. **(2 marks)**

....

2 Write next to each of the see-saws shown below words that describe what will happen when each is released. For example, the see-saw will balance OR the see-saw will turn clockwise OR the see-saw will turn anticlockwise. **(6 marks)**

a

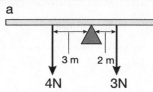

3 m   2 m
4N   3N

b

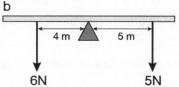

4 m   5 m
6N   5N

c

2 m   3 m
9N   6N

d

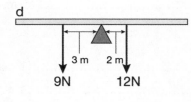

3 m   2 m
9N   12N

e

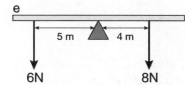

5 m   4 m
6N   8N

f

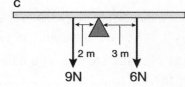

2 m   6 m
12N   4N

Score /11

How well did you do?   ✗ 1–7 **Try again**   8–12 **Getting there**   13–19 **Good work**   20–27 **Excellent!** ✓

Pressure

When forces are concentrated over small areas they create large pressures. When forces are spread out over large areas they create small pressures.

A

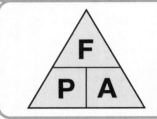

Choose just one answer, a, b, c or d.

1 Which one of the following is an example of force creating low pressure? **(1 mark)**
a) someone wearing snowshoes
b) using a sharp knife
c) the point of a drawing pin
d) the spikes of a sprinter's shoe

2 Which one of the following is an example of forces creating high pressure? **(1 mark)**
a) someone lying on a bed of nails
b) the large feet of a camel
c) the thin handles of a heavy carrier bag
d) someone wearing snowshoes

3 In what units do we measure pressure?
(1 mark)
a) newtons   b) pascals
c) metres   d) newtonmetres

4 To calculate the pressure created by a force we use the equation: **(1 mark)**
a) pressure = force × area
b) pressure = force/area
c) pressure = area/force
d) pressure = force/volume

5 What pressure is created when a force of 500 N is applied over an area of 25 m²? **(1 mark)**
a) 2500 Pa
b) 20 Pa
c) 20 Nm
d) 12,500 Nm

Score   /5

B

Answer all parts of all questions. Show all your working for numerical questions.

1 Which of these statements are true and which are false?

a) Thin handles on a carrier bag are a good idea as they create a high pressure, making it easier to carry them. .... (1 mark)

b) Snowshoes spread forces over a large area. They therefore create low pressures enabling us to walk over snow without sinking into it. .... (1 mark)

c) The pressure created on a nail when hit by a hammer is greatest on the head of the nail. .... (1 mark)

d) Sharp knives create higher pressures than blunt knives. .... (1 mark)

e) Doing press-ups on the palm of your hands creates the same pressure as doing press-ups on your finger tips. .... (1 mark)

2 Calculate the pressure created when:

a) a force of 50 N is applied over an area of 25 m² ....(1 mark)
b) a force of 80 N is applied over an area of 16 m² ....(1 mark)
c) a force of 25 N is applied over an area of 2.5 m² ....(1 mark)

Score   /8

94

These are SATs-style questions. Answer all parts of the questions.

1 The diagram opposite shows a table with very narrow legs standing on a wooden floor.

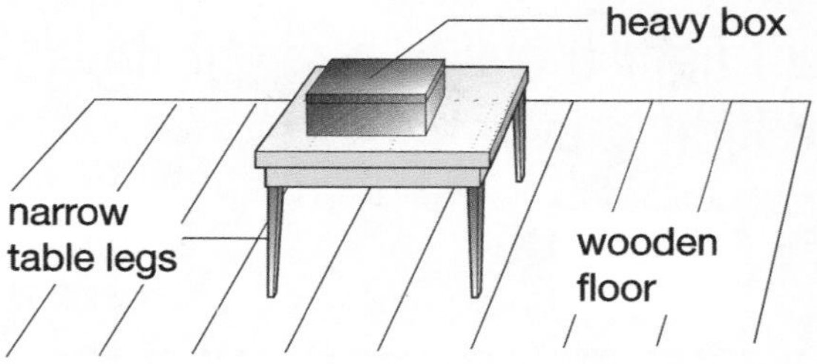

heavy box

narrow table legs

wooden floor

a) Explain why the wooden floor may be damaged if a heavy object is placed on the table. (3 marks)

....

....

b) Explain why placing small wooden mats under each of the wooden legs will prevent the floor from being damaged. (3 marks)

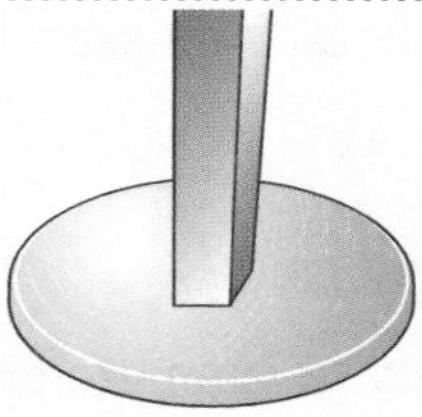

....

....

....

c) Calculate the total pressure exerted on the floor if the object and table weighed 40 N and the total surface area of all the mats was 0.1 m². (3 marks)

....

2 The diagram opposite shows a drawing pin.

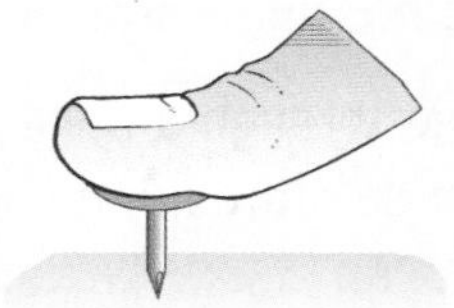

a) Mark with the letter H a place on the picture above where the force applied by the thumb creates a region of high pressure. (1 mark)

b) Mark with the letter L a place on the diagram above where the force applied by the thumb creates a region of low pressure. (1 mark)

c) Name two situations where high pressures are required. (2 marks)

....

d) Name two situations where we want to try to avoid high pressures. (2 marks)

....

Score /15

PRESSURE Physics

For more help on this topic see KS3 Science Success Guide pages 96–97

Light rays and reflection

Rays of light travel in straight lines. We see most objects because of the light they reflect.

A Choose just one answer, a, b, c or d.

1 A luminous object: (1 mark)
a) reflects light   b) gives off light
c) refracts light   d) diffracts light

2 Which of these is an example of a transparent object? (1 mark)
a) a brick   b) a piece of wood
c) a pane of glass   d) a mirror

3 Which of these is an example of an opaque object? (1 mark)
a) a pane of glass   b) a lens
c) a brick   d) a beaker of water

4 We see lightning before we hear the thunder because: (1 mark)
a) sound waves are stronger than light waves
b) sound waves travel faster than light
c) light waves are stronger than sound waves
d) light waves travel faster than sound waves

5 A ray of light strikes the surface of a plane mirror with an angle of incidence of 60°. What is its angle of reflection? (1 mark)
a) 30°   b) 10°
c) 90°   d) 60°

Score   /5

B Answer all parts of all questions.

1 Fill in the missing words. (11 marks)

We can see through a pane of glass because glass is a .... material.
We cannot see through a sheet of steel because steel is an .... material.
If we place an .... object in front of a source of light we can create a ....
An object that emits light like a .... is called a .... object. We see ....
objects because of the .... they reflect.

Shadows have the same .... as the objects that create them. This suggests that ....
travels in ....

2 The diagrams below show rays of light striking plane mirrors. Draw in accurately the reflected ray for each mirror. (4 marks)

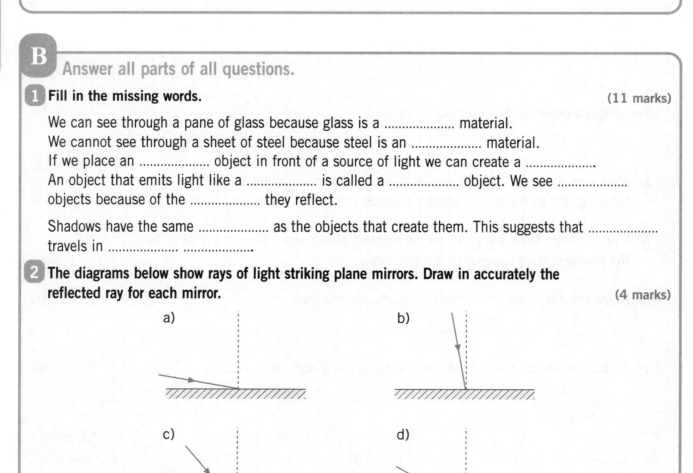

Score   /15

96

C These are SATs-style questions. Answer all parts of the questions.

1 The picture below shows a hand creating a shadow on a wall.

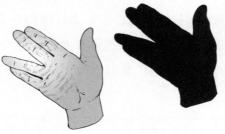

a) What is a shadow? (1 mark)

....

b) Why does the hand create a shadow on the wall? (1 mark)

....

c) What shape does the shadow on the wall have? (1 mark)

....

d) What does the shape of the shadow tell us about light? (1 mark)

....

2 The picture below shows two children playing 'pin the tail on the donkey'.

a) Name one luminous object you can see in the picture. (1 mark)

....

b) Name one non-luminous object you can see in the picture. (1 mark)

....

c) Why is Sally unable to see where she must pin the tail of the donkey? (1 mark)

....

d) Draw rays of light on the picture above showing how David is able to see the
picture of the donkey. (2 marks)

....

Score /9

How well did you do? ✗ 1–8 **Try again** 9–14 **Getting there** 15–21 **Good work** 22–29 **Excellent!** ✓

Refraction and colour

Rays of light travel at different speeds in different media. When they cross the boundary between two media, the change in speed may cause them to change direction. This is called refraction.

A — Choose just one answer, a, b, c or d.

1 When a ray of light enters a glass block it:
a) speeds up   (1 mark)
b) slows down
c) bends away from the normal
d) spreads out

2 When a ray of light enters a glass block at 90° it: (1 mark)
a) speeds up
b) bends away from the normal
c) is not refracted
d) bends towards the normal

3 The splitting of white light into the colours of the rainbow by a prism is called: (1 mark)
a) refraction
b) total internal reflection
c) dispersion
d) resonance

4 What colour(s) is (are) reflected by a blue car in white light?   (1 mark)
a) red   b) green
c) blue   d) all colours

5 What colour light can pass through a red filter?
a) none   b) all   (1 mark)
c) blue   d) red

Score   /5

B — Answer all parts of all questions.

1 When white light travels through a glass prism:

a) which colour is refracted through the largest angle?.. (1 mark)

b) which colour is refracted through the smallest angle?.. (1 mark)

c) Write down in order, the colours of the spectrum produced by the prism.

.... (1 mark)

d) What happens to these colours if a second, inverted prism is placed behind the first?

.... (2 marks)

2 When white light hits a green object, all the colours are absorbed except for green, which is reflected. This is why the object looks green.

On a piece of paper draw diagrams and write a few sentences to explain the appearance of each of the following when seen in white light.

a) a red ball

b) a blue box

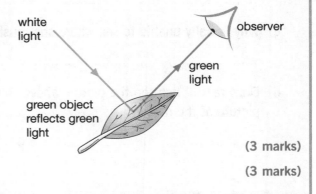

white light

observer

green light

green object reflects green light

(3 marks)

(3 marks)

Score   /11

C These are SATs-style questions. Answer all parts of the questions.

1 The diagram opposite shows a ray of light striking the surface of a glass block.

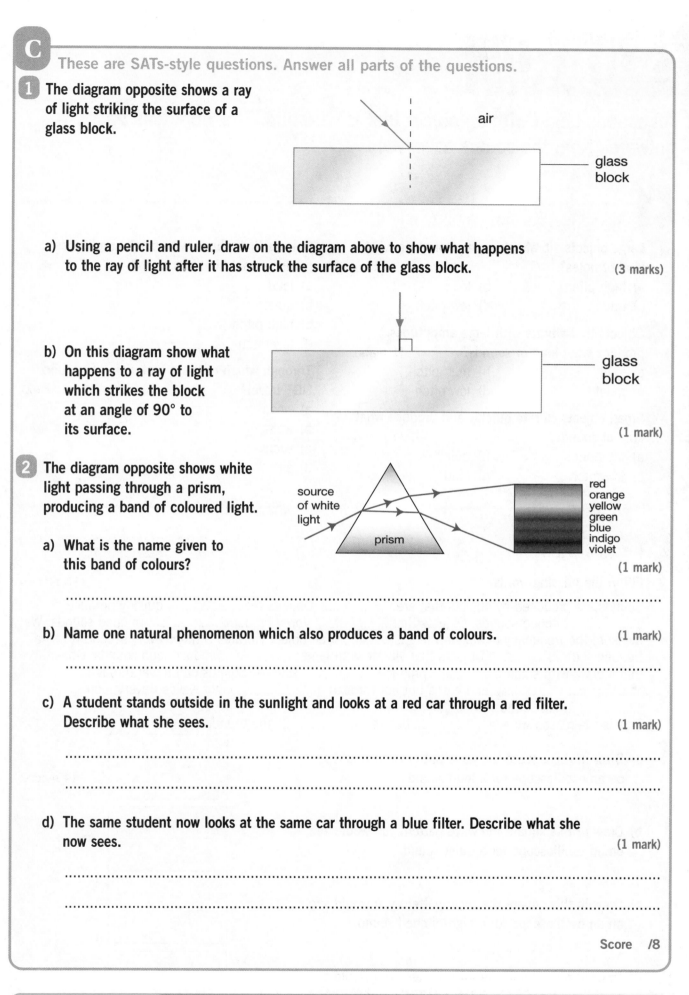

air

glass block

a) Using a pencil and ruler, draw on the diagram above to show what happens to the ray of light after it has struck the surface of the glass block.

(3 marks)

b) On this diagram show what happens to a ray of light which strikes the block at an angle of 90° to its surface.

glass block

(1 mark)

2 The diagram opposite shows white light passing through a prism, producing a band of coloured light.

source of white light

prism

red
orange
yellow
green
blue
indigo
violet

a) What is the name given to this band of colours?

(1 mark)

....

b) Name one natural phenomenon which also produces a band of colours.

(1 mark)

....

c) A student stands outside in the sunlight and looks at a red car through a red filter. Describe what she sees.

(1 mark)

....

....

d) The same student now looks at the same car through a blue filter. Describe what she now sees.

(1 mark)

....

....

Score   /8

How well did you do?   ✗ 1–4 **Try again**   5–9 **Getting there**   10–16 **Good work**   17–24 **Excellent!** ✓

Sounds

All sounds begin with an object that is vibrating. The vibrations travel outwards from the source as waves.

A   Choose just one answer, a, b, c or d.

1 Large objects vibrate slowly and produce what kind of notes?   (1 mark)
a) high pitch   b) loud
c) quiet   d) low pitch

2 Objects that vibrate with large amplitudes produce what kind of sounds?   (1 mark)
a) loud   b) high pitch
c) quiet   d) low pitch

3 Small objects vibrate quickly and produce what kind of sounds?   (1 mark)
a) high pitch   b) quiet
c) low pitch   d) loud

4 Objects that vibrate with small amplitudes produce what kind of sounds?   (1 mark)
a) loud
b) quiet
c) high pitch
d) low pitch

5 Through which of these materials can sound NOT travel?   (1 mark)
a) wood
b) water
c) vacuum
d) air

Score   /5

B   Answer all parts of all questions.

1 Fill in the missing words.   (16 marks)

Sounds are produced by objects that are .... Objects that .... quickly produce .... pitched sounds. Objects that .... slowly produce .... pitched sounds. We measure the frequency of a sound in .... If an object vibrates 5 times every second it has a frequency of .... Objects that vibrate with large .... produce loud sounds. Objects that vibrate with small .... produce .... sounds. Sounds can travel through ...., ... and gases but not through a .... Light waves travel much .... than sound waves.
This is the reason we see .... before we .... the thunder.

2 a) Draw in this square the wave pattern you would see on an oscilloscope for a loud sound.   (4 marks)

b) Draw in this square the wave pattern you would see on an oscilloscope for a quiet sound.

c) Draw in this square the wave pattern you would see on an oscilloscope for a high-pitched sound.

d) Draw in this square the wave pattern you would see on an oscilloscope for a low-pitched sound.

Score   /20

C These are SATs-style questions. Answer all parts of the questions.

1 Linda is standing watching a firework display.

a) Explain why Linda sees the rocket explode and then hears the explosion some time later. (2 marks)

....

....

....

b) What happens to some of the light when it hits the surface of the lake? (1 mark)

....

2 The diagram opposite shows an electric bell inside an air-tight container.

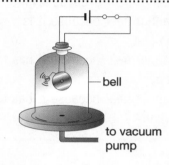

bell

to vacuum pump

a) What does John hear when the switch is closed? (1 mark)

....

b) What does John hear after the vacuum pump has been turned on and all the air removed from the jar? (1 mark)

....

The diagram opposite shows two pupils using a simple string telephone.

c) Explain how the pupil on the left is able to hear the voice of the pupil on the right using the string telephone. (4 marks)

....

....

....

Score /9

How well did you do? ✗ 1–11 **Try again** 12–19 **Getting there** 20–27 **Good work** 28–34 **Excellent!** ✓

Echoes and hearing

When sound waves strike a hard surface they are reflected.
This reflected sound is called an echo.

A Choose just one answer, a, b, c or d.

1 An echo is a sound wave that has been: (1 mark)
   a) reflected   b) refracted
   c) dispersed   d) diffracted

2 If the echo from an echo sounder being used
   by a ship takes a long time to return,
   then the water beneath the ship is: (1 mark)
   a) shallow   b) cold
   c) deep   d) dirty

3 What is ultrasound?   (1 mark)
   a) sound we cannot hear because it is too quiet
   b) sound we cannot hear because it is
      travelling too fast
   c) sound we cannot hear because it has too
      low a frequency
   d) sound we cannot hear because it has too
      high a frequency

4 What is the hearing range of an average
   person?   (1 mark)
   a) 0 – 25 000 Hz
   b) 20 – 20 000 Hz
   c) 20 – 2000 Hz
   d) 25 – 2500 Hz

5 People who work with noisy machinery
   should wear: (1 mark)
   a) hard hats
   b) earphones
   c) ear defenders
   d) gloves

Score   /5

B Answer all parts of all questions.

1 The letters of the words below have become jumbled up. Unscramble the letters, then write
   a sentence that explains the meaning of each word(s).   (8 marks)
   a) soheecs   ....
   b) rason   ....
   c) ssuuntlador ....
   d) rraaggeennhi ....
   e) eeetdlfrc   ....
   f) eeelldiccbas ....
   g) ssunoeld   ....
   h) eeeerrafddns ....

2 We measure the loudness of sounds on the decibel scale.
   An axis for the decibel scale has been drawn opposite.   (6 marks)

   Add the following sounds or sources of sounds
   to the decibel scale to indicate their loudness.
   a) complete silence   b) normal conversation
   c) noisy machinery in a factory   d) a small bird singing
   e) a jet aircraft taking off f) someone whispering

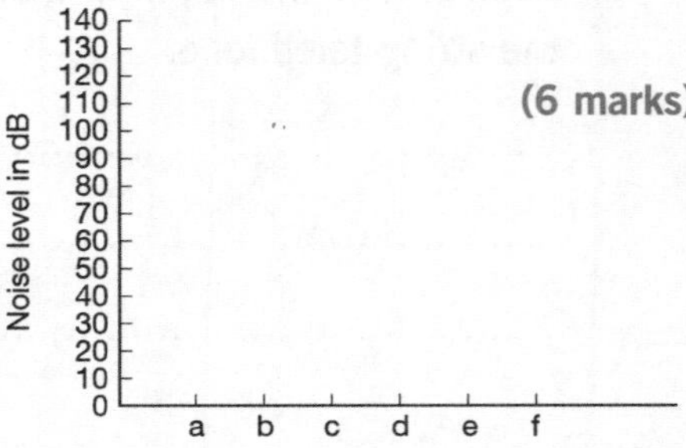

   Noise level in dB
   140 130 120 110 100 90 80 70 60 50 40 30 20 10 0
   a b c d e f

Score   /14

These are SATs-style questions. Answer all parts of the questions.

1 Emma and Clare are testing each other's audible range. They are using a piece of apparatus called a signal generator to produce sounds of different frequencies.

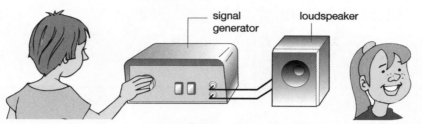

Emma goes first. Clare sets the frequency of the signal generator at 0 Hz and then gradually increases it. Emma tells Clare immediately when she is able to hear the sound. Clare writes down the frequency of the note. Clare then increases the frequency of the note until Emma tells her she can no longer hear it. Clare writes down the frequency of this note. The two girls then repeat the whole experiment, but this time Emma tests Clare's audible range.

The results of the two experiments are shown in the table below.

	Lowest frequency heard in Hz	Highest frequency heard in Hz
Emma	19	20 500
Clare	18	20 100

a) Explain in your own words the meaning of the phrase 'audible range.' (2 marks)

....

b) What was the lowest frequency that Emma could hear? (1 mark)

....

c) What was the highest frequency Clare could hear? (1 mark)

....

d) Who had the widest audible range, Emma or Clare? (1 mark)

....

e) What do we call sounds that have frequencies too high for humans to hear? (1 mark)

....

f) Name two animals that can hear sounds with too high a frequency for humans to hear. (2 marks)

....

2 The picture opposite shows a pair of ear defenders.

a) Give one example of a person who should wear ear defenders whilst working. (1 mark)

....

b) What might happen to this worker if he does not wear ear defenders? (1 mark)

....

Score /10

How well did you do?   ✗ 1–8 **Try again**   9–14 **Getting there**   15–21 **Good work**   22–29 **Excellent!** ✓

For more help on this topic see KS3 Science Success Guide pages 104–105

Energy

We all need energy to be able to do things. We get this energy from the food we eat. Food is a form of chemical energy, but there are other sources and forms of energy.

A Choose just one answer, a, b, c or d.

1 Which of the following is not a type of energy?
(1 mark)
a) electrical   b) nuclear
c) sound   d) power

2 Which of the following is not a type of stored energy?
(1 mark)
a) chemical
b) gravitational potential
c) elastic potential   d) sound

3 What kind of energy is stored in food? (1 mark)
a) chemical   b) nuclear
c) light   d) heat

4 What kind of energy is stored in a wound-up clockwork toy?
(1 mark)
a) kinetic
b) elastic potential
c) gravitational potential
d) thermal

5 An object has kinetic energy when: (1 mark)
a) the Sun is shining
b) it is high up
c) it is moving
d) it is stretched

Score /5

B Answer all parts of all questions.

1 Draw a line connecting each word to the correct explanation.
The first one has been done for you.
(9 marks)

gravitational potential energy	The energy an object has because it is moving.
stored energy	The energy produced by reactions in the centre of an atom.
sound energy	Vibrating objects are sources of this energy.
nuclear energy	Forms of energy that are waiting to be used.
electrical energy	Food is an example of this.
kinetic energy	This energy is available every time a current flows.
chemical energy	Winding up a spring will give it this type of energy.
elastic potential energy	Most of our energy on the Earth begins as this.
light energy	When one type of energy changes into another type of energy.
energy transfer	The energy an object has when it is high up.

B (Continued)

2 **Put the words in each of the groups below into the correct order.** (3 marks)

a) into candle energy energy and chemical light heat burning changes a.

....

b) sound a energy changes loudspeaker electrical into.

....

c) stores energy a battery chemical.

....

Score /12

C

These are SATs-style questions. Answer all parts of the questions.

1 **The diagrams below show some energy changes taking place.**

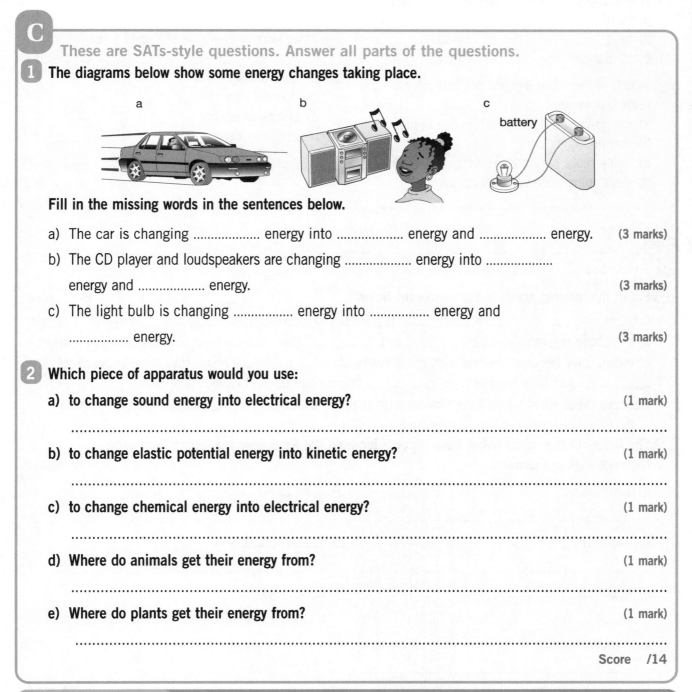

a   b   c

Fill in the missing words in the sentences below.

a) The car is changing .... energy into .... energy and .... energy. (3 marks)

b) The CD player and loudspeakers are changing .... energy into ....
energy and .... energy. (3 marks)

c) The light bulb is changing .... energy into .... energy and
.... energy. (3 marks)

2 **Which piece of apparatus would you use:**

a) to change sound energy into electrical energy? (1 mark)

....

b) to change elastic potential energy into kinetic energy? (1 mark)

....

c) to change chemical energy into electrical energy? (1 mark)

....

d) Where do animals get their energy from? (1 mark)

....

e) Where do plants get their energy from? (1 mark)

....

Score /14

How well did you do? ✗ 1–11 Try again   12–19 Getting there   20–26 Good work   27–31 Excellent! ✓

Using energy resources

Fossil fuels are one of our most concentrated sources of energy.
We use a large amount of fossil fuel to generate our electricity.

A Choose just one answer, a, b, c or d.

1 Which of these is not a fossil fuel? **(1 mark)**
a) oil   b) coal
c) gas   d) wood

2 How many years does it take for fossil fuels to form? **(1 mark)**
a) tens   b) hundreds
c) thousands d) millions

3 Which of the following will not make fossil fuels last longer? **(1 mark)**
a) improving heat insulation in the home
b) driving bigger cars
c) using more public transport
d) developing more efficient car engines

4 How is the energy released from a fuel?
a) digging it up   **(1 mark)**
b) storing it in tanks
c) burning it
d) filtering it

5 What kind of energy is stored in a fuel?
(1 mark)
a) heat energy
b) thermal energy
c) chemical energy
d) nuclear energy

Score   /5

B Answer all parts of all questions.

1 Fill in the missing words in the sentences below. **(10 marks)**

Coal, oil and .... are .... fuels. They are concentrated .... of energy. They are formed from the remains of .... and .... that died millions of years ago. But instead of rotting they became covered with many layers of .... As a result they were under great .... and they were at high .... These conditions changed them into .... fuels. Because these fuels take a long time to form they are called .... fuels.

2 The letters of the words below have become jumbled up. Rearrange the letters then write the meanings of the words. **(7 marks)**

a) sssfflloeui

....

c) iiaadrcn

....

e) oponilltu

....

g) nnneeebolawr

....

b) oottnaprewsi

....

d) eeeeefftuoghcrs

....

f) eeeanrlbw

....

Score   /17

106

C These are SATs-style questions. Answer all parts of the questions.

1 Natural gas is a non-renewable source of energy.

a) Tick the boxes of two other non-renewable sources of energy. (2 marks)

wood ☐   oil ☐

Sun ☐   battery ☐

coal ☐   straw ☐

b) Why is natural gas described as a non-renewable source of energy? (1 mark)

....

c) What kind of energy is stored in natural gas? (1 mark)

....

d) How is the energy stored in natural gas released? (1 mark)

....

e) Where did the energy stored in natural gas originally come from? (1 mark)

....

2 The diagram below shows the energy changes that take place in a power station that uses natural gas for its fuel.

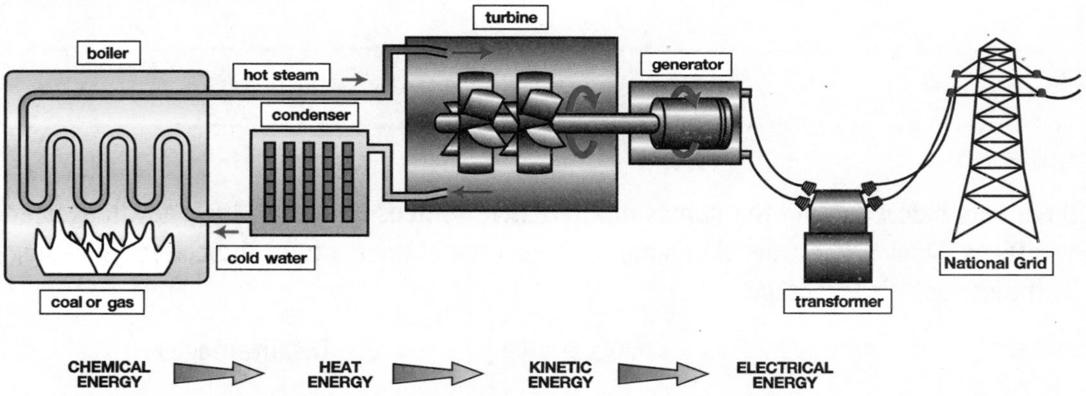

boiler   turbine   generator

hot steam →

condenser

cold water

coal or gas

National Grid

transformer

CHEMICAL ENERGY ⇒ HEAT ENERGY ⇒ KINETIC ENERGY ⇒ ELECTRICAL ENERGY

a) What is the energy released from the natural gas used for? (1 mark)

....

b) What energy transfer takes place when the steam enters the turbine housing? (2 marks)

....

c) What energy transfer takes place when the turbine turns the generator? (2 marks)

....

d) Suggest two ways in which we could make non-renewable fuels last longer. (2 marks)

....

Score   /13

How well did you do? ✗ 1–9 Try again   10–19 Getting there   20–27 Good work   28–35 Excellent! ✓

Alternative sources of energy

Burning fossil fuels in large quantities creates many problems including acid rain, the Greenhouse Effect and exhaustion of valuable non-renewable fuel. One way to reduce these problems is to use alternative sources of energy.

A Choose just one answer, a, b, c or d.

1 Which of the following is not a renewable source of energy? **(1 mark)**
a) oil   b) wind
c) waves   d) solar

2 Which of the following is not affected by the weather? **(1 mark)**
a) solar energy   b) wind energy
c) wave energy   d) geothermal energy

3 Which of the following does not use water as its source of energy? **(1 mark)**
a) tidal energy   b) hydroelectricity
c) biomass   d) wave energy

4 Which of the following does not have a high initial cost? **(1 mark)**
a) hydroelectricity
b) tidal energy
c) geothermal energy
d) biomass

5 Which of the following uses the energy stored in living matter? **(1 mark)**
a) solar energy
b) wind energy
c) tidal energy
d) biomass

Score   /5

B Answer all parts of the questions.

1 The three lists below contain the names of alternative sources of energy, their advantages and their disadvantages. Draw a line from the name of the source of energy to a) the correct advantage and b) the correct disadvantage. **(10 marks)**

Advantages	Energy source	Disadvantages
Reliable, two tides per day	geothermal	Obstacle to water transport
Low-level technology	tidal	Poor energy capture
Useful for isolated islands	wind	Possible visual and noise pollution
No pollution or environmental problems	hydroelectric	Very few suitable sites
Energy can be stored until required	wave	High cost to environment, i.e. flooding

Score   /10

C   These are SATs-style questions. Answer all parts of the questions.

1 A – wood   B – coal   C – solar   D – wind

Answer A, B, C or D to the following questions.

a) Name one non-renewable fuel.   (1 mark)

    ....

b) Name one renewable biomass fuel.   (1 mark)

    ....

c) Name two sources of energy which depend directly on the weather conditions, that if
    the conditions are not correct they produce no energy.   (2 marks)

    ....

d) Suggest two ways in which we could reduce the amount of fossil fuels we burn. (2 marks)

    ....

2 The diagram below shows a simple hydroelectric power station.

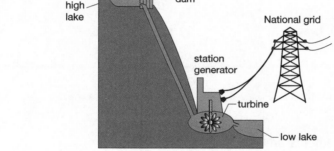

a) What kind of energy does the water in the high lake have?   (1 mark)

    ....

b) What kind of energy does the water gain as it falls from the high lake towards the
    generating station and the lower lake?   (1 mark)

    ....

c) What energy change takes place in the generating station?   (1 mark)

    ....

d) Name two other sources that use 'water energy'.   (2 marks)

    ....

                                                                        Score   /11

How well did you do?   ✗ 1–7 Try again   8–12 Getting there   13–19 Good work   20–26 Excellent! ✓

Heat transfer

Heat flows when there is a temperature difference between two places. It flows from the hotter to the cooler place. Three methods by which it can do this are conduction, convection and radiation.

A Choose just one answer, a, b, c or d.

1 Heat will flow: (1 mark)
- a) from a hotter place to a cooler place
- b) from a cooler place to a hotter place
- c) from dark objects to light objects
- d) downhill

2 Which of the following is a good conductor of heat?   (1 mark)
- a) wood
- b) plastic
- c) cement
- d) copper

3 Which of the following is an insulator? (1 mark)
- a) copper
- b) plastic
- c) aluminium
- d) brass

4 Woven materials such as wool and cotton are excellent insulators because: (1 mark)
- a) they are natural materials
- b) they contain trapped air
- c) they are man-made materials
- d) they are soft

5 Transfer of heat by convection cannot take place in: (1 mark)
- a) liquids
- b) gases
- c) fluids
- d) solids

Score   /5

B Answer all parts of the question.

1 Which of the following statements are true and which are false.

a) Heat will flow to a hot place from a cooler place. .... (1 mark)

b) Metals are good conductors of heat. .... (1 mark)

c) Saucepans have plastic handles because plastics are good conductors of heat. .... (1 mark)

d) Gases are excellent insulators. .... (1 mark)

e) Convection currents can move heat in solids and liquids. .... (1 mark)

f) Houses are painted white in hot countries in order to reflect radiation and so stay cool. .... (1 mark)

g) Heat in the form of radiation can travel through a window with double glazing. .... (1 mark)

h) Heat energy travels to the Earth from the Sun by conduction. .... (1 mark)

i) The particles at the hot end of a metal rod vibrate vigorously. .... (1 mark)

j) Woven materials such as wool and cotton contain trapped air and so are excellent insulators. .... (1 mark)

k) Plastic table mats are good insulators. They prevent heat from hot food reaching and damaging the table top. .... (1 mark)

l) A thick piece of glass is a better insulator than two thin ones with a layer of air between them. .... (1 mark)

m) The hottest tea in a cup will be at the top. .... (1 mark)

n) A black car will absorb less heat radiation than a white car and will therefore remain cooler. .... (1 mark)

Score   /14

These are SATs-style questions. Answer all parts of the questions.

1 The picture opposite shows the apparatus being used by two pupils, Katy and Richard.

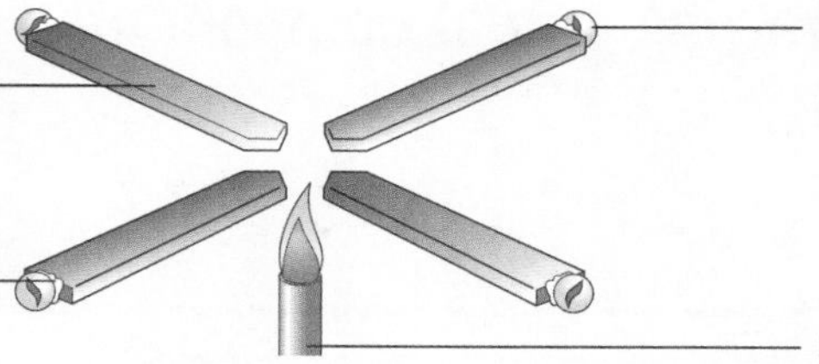

metal bar (each bar is a different metal)

marble

wax attaching marble to bar

Bunsen burner

a) How does heat from the Bunsen burner travel along the bars? (1 mark)

....

b) Explain what happens to the marbles after the Bunsen burner has been turned on for several minutes. (1 mark)

....

c) How can the pupils tell from this experiment which of the four different metals is the best conductor of heat? (1 mark)

....

d) Give one use for a material that is a good conductor. (1 mark)

....

e) Give one use for a material that is a very poor conductor. (1 mark)

....

2 The picture opposite shows a house that has not been insulated.

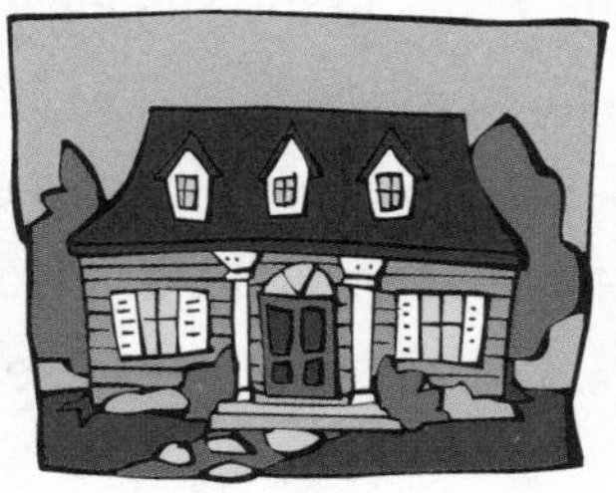

a) Suggest one way in which we could reduce the amount of heat escaping through the roof. (1 mark)

....

b) Suggest one way to reduce the amount of heat escaping through the walls. (1 mark)

....

c) Suggest one way in which we could reduce the amount of heat escaping through the windows. (1 mark)

....

d) Suggest one way in which we could reduce the amount of heat escaping through the floors. (1 mark)

....

e) Suggest one way in which we could reduce the amount of heat escaping through cracks and gaps around the doors and windows. (1 mark)

....

Score /10

HEAT TRANSFER Physics

How well did you do? ✗ 1–8 **Try again** 9–14 **Getting there** 15–21 **Good work** 22–29 **Excellent!** ✓

Circuits and components

Instead of drawing actual components we use circuit diagrams with easy to draw symbols.

A Choose just one answer, a, b, c or d.

1 An electric current is a flow of: (1 mark)
   a) atoms   b) charge
   c) neutrons   d) volts

2 Charges can be made to move using: (1 mark)
   a) wires   b) resistors
   c) cells   d) switches

3 What are charges given as they pass through batteries?   (1 mark)
   a) energy   b) more charge
   c) insulation   d) resistance

4 Several cells connected together make an:
   a) a battery   (1 mark)
   b) a resistor
   c) a voltmeter
   d) a conductor

5 A complete circuit is one which: (1 mark)
   a) has no gaps
   b) has a cell
   c) has a battery
   d) contains bulbs

Score /5

B Answer all parts of all questions.

1 Fill in the missing words in the sentences below.   (8 marks)

An electric current is a flow of .... The .... are given energy and made to flow using a .... or a .... Charges can flow easily through connecting .... The wires and all the other components make a loop called a .... If there are no gaps the loop is called a .... If there are gaps it is called an ....

2 The names of some common circuit components and their symbols are shown below.
Draw a line connecting the name of each component with its circuit symbol.
The first one has been done for you.   (7 marks)

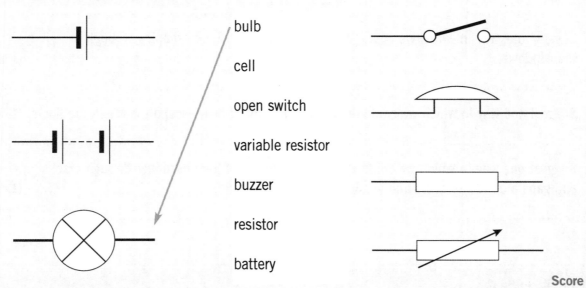

bulb

cell

open switch

variable resistor

buzzer

resistor

battery

Score /15

C

This is a SATs-style question. Answer all parts of the question.

1 Linda and Julie have built the circuit shown opposite. They are going to use it to test different materials in order to discover if they are conductors or insulators.

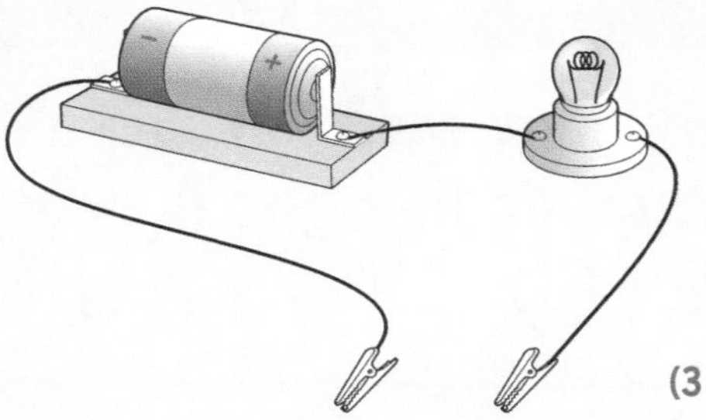

a) Explain how Linda and Julie use the circuit to test the different materials. (3 marks)

....

....

....

b) The table below shows some of the materials the two students tested.

Material	Conductor	Insulator
copper	✔	
steel		
paper		
bronze		
graphite		
mercury		

Put a tick in the second column if you think the material is a conductor and in the third column if you think the material is an insulator. The first one has been done for you. (5 marks)

Linda and Julie build a second circuit similar to the one shown opposite.

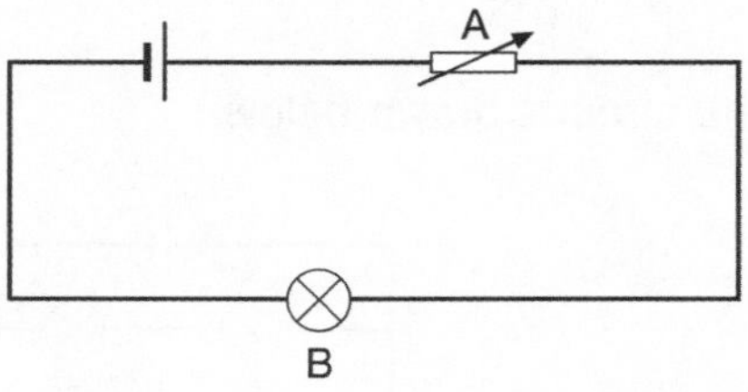

c) What is A in the above circuit? (1 mark)

....

d) What is B in the above circuit? (1 mark)

....

e) What happens to the appearance of B if the value of A is increased? (1 mark)

....

f) What happens to B if a second identical cell, pumping in the same direction as the first, is added to the circuit? (1 mark)

....

g) What happens to B if one of the cells is connected in the opposite direction? (1 mark)

....

Score /13

How well did you do? ✗ 1–11 Try again 12–21 Getting there 22–27 Good work 28–33 Excellent! ✓

For more help on this topic see KS3 Science Success Guide pages 114–115

Circuits – current and voltage

Currents carry energy around a circuit. They receive this energy from a cell or battery and then give it away to the different components in the circuit.

A

Choose just one answer, a, b, c or d.

1 A series circuit has no: (1 mark)
 a) gaps b) cell
 c) resistor d) branches

2 A parallel circuit has: (1 mark)
 a) bulbs b) batteries
 c) gaps d) junctions

3 The current in a series circuit: (1 mark)
 a) gets smaller as it moves away from the cell or battery
 b) always flows clockwise
 c) gets bigger as it moves away from the cell or battery
 d) is the same everywhere

4 We measure the current flowing through a wire using: (1 mark)
 a) an ammeter
 b) a voltmeter
 c) a joulemeter
 d) a pedometer

5 As charges move around a circuit they give away: (1 mark)
 a) charge
 b) current
 c) energy
 d) resistance

Score /5

B

Answer all parts of the question.

1 Look at the circuits drawn below.

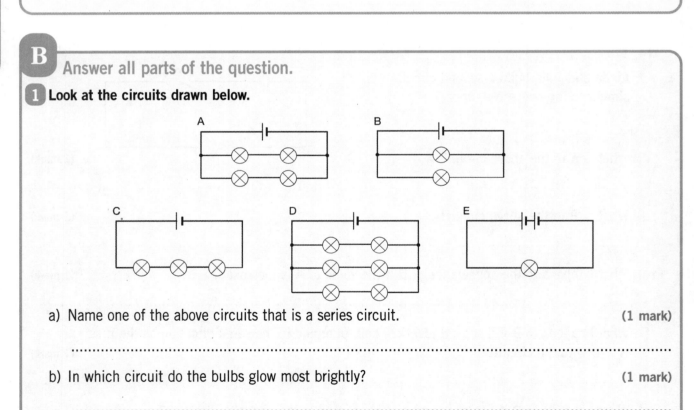

a) Name one of the above circuits that is a series circuit. (1 mark)

....

b) In which circuit do the bulbs glow most brightly? (1 mark)

....

c) In which circuit do the bulbs glow least brightly? (1 mark)

....

Score /3

114

C

These are SATs-style questions. Answer all parts of the questions.

1 The diagram below shows a circuit containing 3 switches and 4 bulbs.

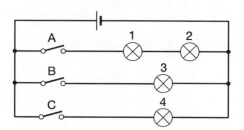

a) Which bulbs glow when switch A is closed and switches B and C are open?   (2 marks)

....

b) Which bulbs glow when switches A and B are closed and switch C is open?   (3 marks)

....

c) Which switch must be closed if bulb 4 is to glow and bulbs 1, 2 and 3 are to remain off?   (1 mark)

....

2 The diagram opposite shows a circuit containing a cell, a switch, three ammeters, a resistor and a bulb.

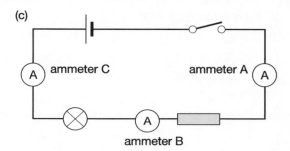

When the switch is closed the reading on ammeter A is 0.6 A.

a) What is the reading on ammeter B?   (1 mark)

....

b) What is the reading on ammeter C?   (1 mark)

....

The diagram opposite shows a second circuit containing a cell, a switch, three ammeters, a resistor and a bulb.

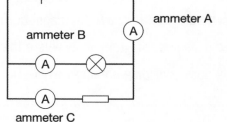

When the switch is closed the reading on ammeter A is 0.9 A and the reading on ammeter B is 0.6 A.

c) What is the reading on ammeter C?   (1 mark)

....

d) What energy transfer takes place when current passes through a bulb?   (3 marks)

....

Score   /12

How well did you do?   1–4 Try again   5–9 Getting there   10–14 Good work   15–20 Excellent! ✓

Magnets and electromagnets

Magnets attract magnetic materials. Electromagnets made from coils of wire and soft iron cores also attract magnetic materials.

A Choose just one answer, a, b, c or d.

1 Which of the following is a magnetic material?

(1 mark)

a) paper
b) plastic
c) steel
d) brass

2 Which of the following is a non-magnetic material?

(1 mark)

a) copper
b) iron
c) nickel
d) steel

3 If two similar magnetic poles are placed next to each other they will:

(1 mark)

a) attract
b) become warm
c) move together
d) repel

4 Give one advantage of an electromagnet compared with a permanent magnet. (1 mark)

a) it is smaller
b) it can be turned on and off
c) it is quicker to use
d) it creates less pollution

5 Which one of the following will not increase the strength of an electromagnet? (1 mark)

a) using a larger current
b) adding more turns
c) using thicker wire
d) adding a soft iron core

Score /5

B Answer all parts of all questions.

1 a) Name 3 magnetic materials. .... (3 marks)

b) Name 3 non-magnetic materials. ....(3 marks)

c) Explain how the north pole of a magnet got its name.. (1 mark)

d) Draw a diagram of two bar magnets showing how they should be arranged if they are to repel each other. .... (1 mark)

e) Draw a diagram to show the magnetic field around a bar magnet.................................... (1 mark)

f) How does your diagram show where the magnetic field is strong? .... (1 mark)

g) How does your diagram show where the magnetic field is weak? .... (1 mark)

....

2 The word search opposite contains ten words connected with magnetism. See if you can find them all.

(10 marks)

```
L M U C V Z R E P E L T E
P M A G N E T I C O I L L
P A T T R A C T O P R Q X
R B F O C O R E M B X Q A
O D I A I R O N P O L E P
E L E C T R O M A G N E T
A P L R P T S O S N R I Q
S T D X B Y K M S W Y A C
```

Score /21

116

C

These are SATs-style questions. Answer all parts of the questions.

1 The diagram below shows a simple electromagnet.

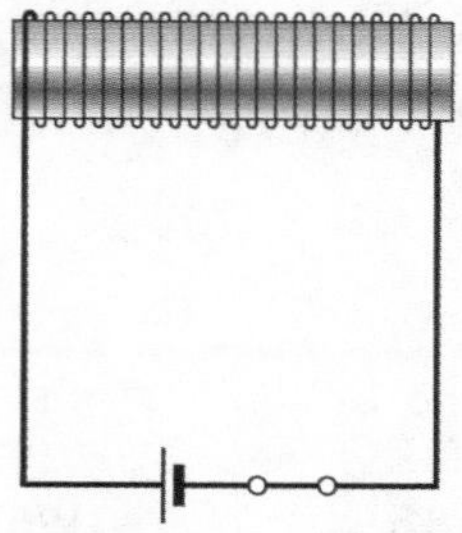

a) Add lines of force to the diagram above to show the shape of the magnetic field around the electromagnet. (3 marks)

b) Give two ways in which the strength of an electromagnet can be increased. (2 marks)

....

....

c) Give one advantage of an electromagnet over a permanent magnet. (1 mark)

....

2 The diagram opposite shows a simple electromagnet being used to separate different types of metal.

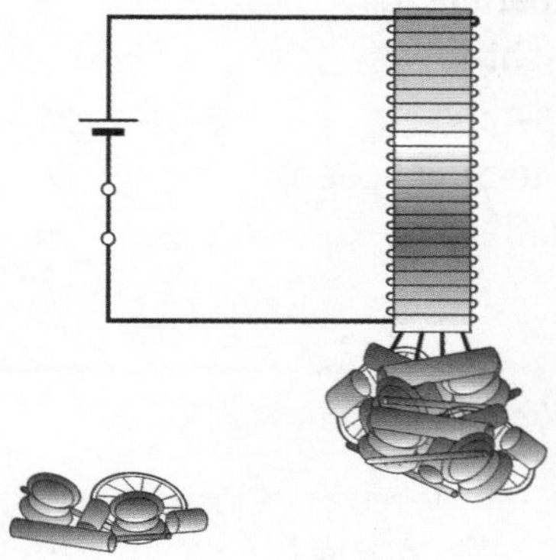

a) What will happen when the electromagnet is turned on and then placed near a piece of steel? (1 mark)

....

b) What will happen when the electromagnet is turned on and then placed near a piece of aluminium? (1 mark)

....

c) Give two other uses for electromagnets. (2 marks)

....

....

Score /10

How well did you do? 1–7 Try again 8–18 Getting there 19–28 Good work 29–36 Excellent!

For more help on this topic see KS3 Science Success Guide pages 118–119

The Earth in space

We live on a planet called the Earth. Our planet is rotating and at the same time orbiting the Sun. There are a total of nine planets in our Solar System.

A Choose just one answer, a, b, c or d.

1 We experience day and night on the Earth because: **(1 mark)**
a) the Earth is spinning
b) the Earth is tilted
c) the Earth is round
d) the Moon orbits the Earth

2 The time it takes the Earth to make one complete rotation is: **(1 mark)**
a) one year
b) one day
c) one season
d) one month

3 The part of the Earth facing away from the Sun is experiencing: **(1 mark)**
a) night-time
b) daytime
c) a total eclipse
d) winter

4 Which of the following is untrue? **(1 mark)**
a) the Sun follows the same path in the winter as in the summer
b) the Sun rises in the east
c) the Sun sets in the west
d) the Sun's path goes high across the sky in the summer

5 When we in Britain are having our winter: **(1 mark)**
a) the northern part of the Earth is tilted away from the Sun
b) the southern part of the Earth is tilted away from the Sun
c) people in Australia are also having their winter
d) the Sun's path goes high across the sky

Score /5

B Answer all parts of the question.

1 The diagram below shows our Solar System. **(11 marks)**

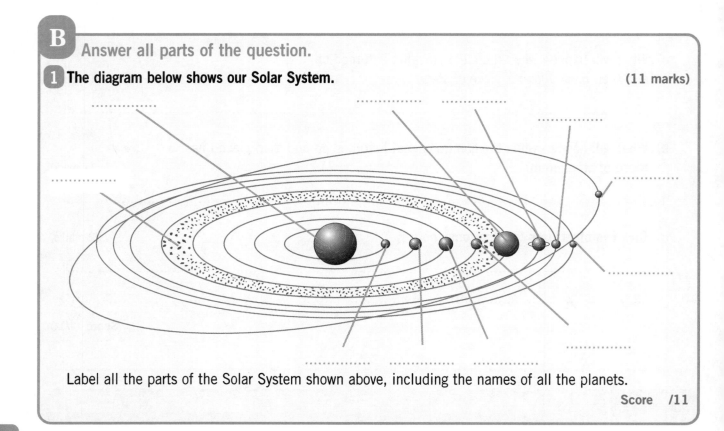

Label all the parts of the Solar System shown above, including the names of all the planets.

Score /11

C These are SATs-style questions. Answer all parts of the questions.

1 The diagram below shows the path followed by the Sun across the sky in the summer.

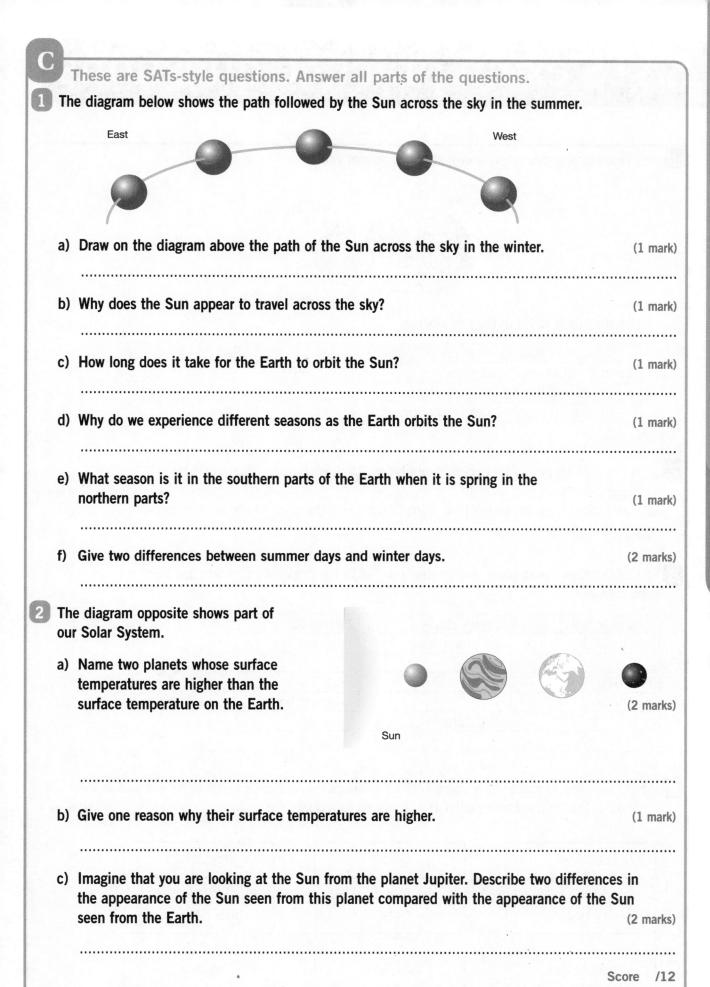

East   West

a) Draw on the diagram above the path of the Sun across the sky in the winter.   (1 mark)

....

b) Why does the Sun appear to travel across the sky?   (1 mark)

....

c) How long does it take for the Earth to orbit the Sun?   (1 mark)

....

d) Why do we experience different seasons as the Earth orbits the Sun?   (1 mark)

....

e) What season is it in the southern parts of the Earth when it is spring in the
northern parts?   (1 mark)

....

f) Give two differences between summer days and winter days.   (2 marks)

....

2 The diagram opposite shows part of
our Solar System.

a) Name two planets whose surface
temperatures are higher than the
surface temperature on the Earth.   (2 marks)

Sun

....

b) Give one reason why their surface temperatures are higher.   (1 mark)

....

c) Imagine that you are looking at the Sun from the planet Jupiter. Describe two differences in
the appearance of the Sun seen from this planet compared with the appearance of the Sun
seen from the Earth.   (2 marks)

....

Score   /12

SATS exam practice questions

1 The labelled diagram below shows a typical animal cell.

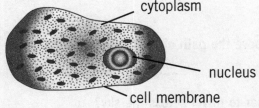

Use the labels to fill in the table below.

(3 marks)

Function	Part
controls all the cell's activities	
where chemical reactions take place	
controls what passes in and out of the cell	

2 a) A piece of copper metal is heated until it melts. The change of state that takes place is from .... to ....

(2 marks)

b) 5 g of copper was heated until it melted. What was the mass of the melted copper?
.... g

(1 mark)

3 The table below shows some energy changes. Fill in the gaps. The first one has been done for you.

(7 marks)

Energy in	Energy changer	Energy out
electrical	light bulb	heat and light
	radio	
electrical		heat
chemical		heat and light
	wind turbine	
light		electrical

4 Metals are used to make many objects. Draw a line to connect each metal to its use and to the property of that metal which makes it suitable for that particular use.

(6 marks)

bridges	copper	lightweight
drinks cans	iron	does not react
water pipes	aluminium	strong

5 **a)** **Using the words below, label the diagram of the breathing system.** (6 marks)
trachea   alveoli   bronchioles   bronchi   diaphragm   intercostal muscles

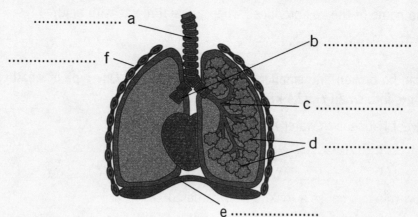

.... a

b ....

f ....

c ....

d ....

e ....

b) Which of the two labelled parts work together to help us breathe in and out? (2 marks)

....

c) What is the name of the organ in the diagram that lies between the lungs? (1 mark)

....

6 **The diagram opposite shows the colour triangle.**

The table below shows what happens when different coloured lights overlap. Use the colour triangle to fill in the gaps in the table below.

(6 marks)

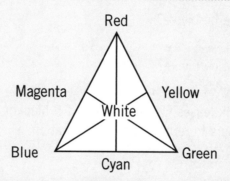

Colour A	Colour B	Colour A + Colour B
red	green	
red	blue	
blue	green	
blue	yellow	
green	magenta	
cyan	red	

7 **The table below shows how four metals reacted with acid.**

Metal	Reaction with acid
A	no reaction
B	violent reaction
C	quick reaction
D	slow reaction

a) Use the table above to place the metals in order of reactivity. (4 marks)

Most reactive   ....

....

....

Least reactive   ....

b) Use the table to suggest which of the metals could be gold. (1 mark)

....

c) Use the table to suggest which of the metals could be potassium.   (1 mark)

....

d) What is the name of the gas produced when a metal reacts with acid?   (1 mark)

....

8 Large rocks can be broken into smaller pieces by weathering. One type of weathering involves water. The water enters into small cracks in rocks.

a) Describe what happens to water as it freezes to form ice.   (1 mark)

....

....

b) Explain how this can cause a rock to be weathered.   (1 mark)

....

....

9 The following is a food chain from a woodland.

oak leaves ⇒ woodlouse ⇒ blackbird

a) Which animal is a herbivore?   (1 mark)

....

b) Which animal is a carnivore?   (1 mark)

....

c) There were 20 oak leaves, 10 woodlice and 5 blackbirds in this food chain. Draw a pyramid of numbers to represent this information.   (2 marks)

10 Kevin has a new blue pen. He uses chromatography to investigate the ink in his new pen. His experiment is shown opposite.

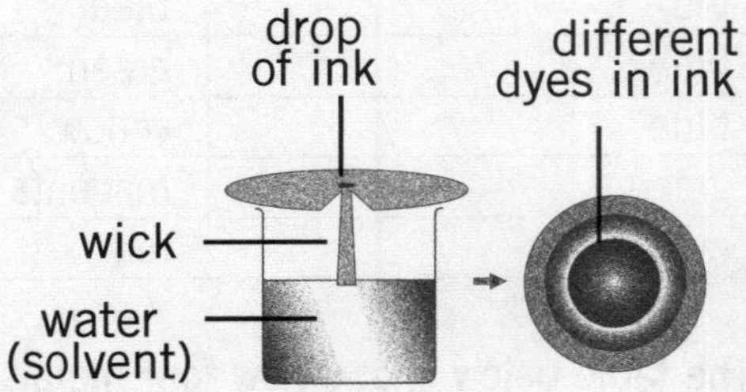

drop of ink

different dyes in ink

wick

water (solvent)

a) Why did Kevin use filter paper in his experiment?   (1 mark)

....

....

b) Why did Kevin draw a line across the bottom of his chromatogram using a pencil and not a pen?   (1 mark)

....

c) How could Kevin tell how many different coloured substances were present in the ink of his new pen?   (1 mark)

....

....

11 The table below shows what happens when different coloured lights try to pass through a coloured filter. Use the colour triangle in Q6 to fill in the gaps. (5 marks)

Colour of light	Colour of filter	Colour of light that passes through filter
white	red	
blue	red	
yellow	red	
magenta	blue	
green	cyan	

12 Alistair is given a pile of objects made from steel, copper and wood.

a) Suggest one way in which Alistair could separate the steel objects from those made of copper and wood. (1 mark)

....

b) Suggest one way in which Alistair could separate the copper objects from those made of wood. (1 mark)

....

c) Alistair builds an electrical circuit similar to that shown opposite. Explain how he could use this circuit to discover which of the three materials in his pile are conductors and which are insulators. (4 marks)

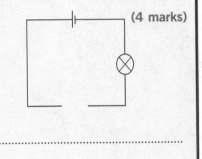

....

....

....

....

13 a) Shelley and Peter carried out some food tests on a cheese sandwich to see what nutrients it contained. The results were as follows: (4 marks)

cheese – changed Biuret's solution from blue to purple, and when tested with ethanol and water the solution turned cloudy

butter – when tested with ethanol and water the solution turned cloudy

bread – turned iodine solution a blue-black colour

From these results what nutrients did they contain? Put a tick in the correct column.

	Protein	Fat	Starch
cheese			
butter			
bread			

b) Adding Benedict's solution and heating a food sample is the test for glucose. The solution is a blue colour to begin with. What colour does it change to if glucose is present? (1 mark)

....

14 Sue placed a small piece of magnesium metal into some blue copper sulphate solution. Complete the equation below to show the reaction in Sue's experiment.

a) Magnesium + copper sulphate → .... + ...   (2 marks)

b) Sue noticed that a brown substance now coated the magnesium metal. What was the brown substance?   (1 mark)

....

15 The diagram below shows the circuit used for an electric bell. Explain in detail what happens when the bell-push is pressed.   (4 marks)

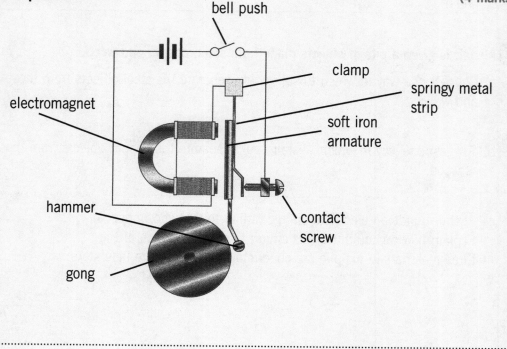

....

....

....

16 The diagram opposite shows a synovial joint in the body.

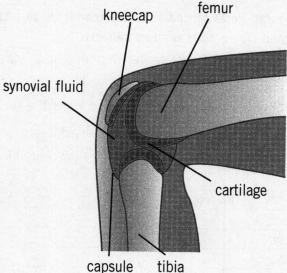

a) What is the function of the synovial fluid?   (1 mark)

....

b) What is the function of cartilage?   (1 mark)

....

17 a) The diagram below is a leaf, the organ of photosynthesis.

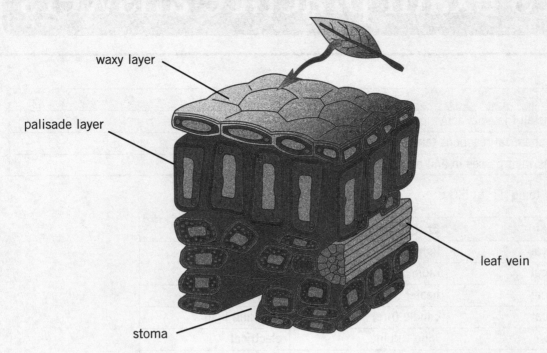

Look at the labelled parts and decide which part matches which function by drawing four lines. **(4 marks)**

stoma   prevents the leaf from losing too much water
waxy layer   the place where most photosynthesis takes place
palisade layer   transports water and minerals to the leaf
leaf vein   where carbon dioxide enters the leaf

b) What else apart from water and carbon dioxide does a leaf need to be able to photosynthesise? **(2 marks)**

....

....

SATS exam practice answers

1	Function	Part
	controls all the cells activities	**nucleus**
	where chemical reactions take place	**cytoplasm**
	controls what passes in and out of the cell	**cell membrane**

2 a) solid to liquid b) 5.0 g

3	Energy in	Energy changer	Energy out
	electrical	light bulb	heat and light
	electrical	radio	**sound**
	electrical	**heater (resistor)**	heat
	chemical	**candle (fire)**	heat and light
	kinetic	wind turbine	**electrical**
	light	**solar cell**	electrical

4 copper – water pipes – does not react/iron – bridges – strong/aluminium – drinks cans – lightweight

5 a) A = trachea B = bronchi C = bronchiole D = alveoli E = diaphragm F = intercostal muscle
   b) diaphragm and intercostal muscles c) the heart

6	Colour A	Colour B	Colour A + Colour B
	red	green	**yellow**
	red	blue	**magenta**
	blue	green	**cyan**
	blue	yellow	**white**
	green	magenta	**white**
	cyan	red	**white**

7 a) B, C, D, A   b) A   c) B   d) hydrogen
8 a) it expands   b) the ice expands and forces the existing crack further apart
9 a) woodlouse   b) blackbird
   c) 1 mark for a pyramid drawn in proportion (i.e. larger at the bottom and narrowing up to the third layer, representing the numbers 20 at the bottom then 10 then 5 at the top), 1 mark for labelling the layers oak leaves, woodlice and blackbird
10 a) filter paper is porous   b) pencil is insoluble/pen is soluble
   c) Kevin should count the number of different coloured inks that develop on his chromatogram

11	Colour of light	Colour of filter	Colour of light that passes through filter
	white	red	**red**
	blue	red	**none**
	yellow	red	**red**
	magenta	blue	**blue**
	green	cyan	**green**

12 a) he could use a magnet which would attract just the pieces of steel

b) he could put them into a bowl of water; the wooden pieces will float and the copper pieces will sink

c) with the circuit incomplete the bulb does not light (1), if a conductor is placed across the gap the circuit is complete (1) and the bulb will glow (1), if an insulator is placed across the gap the bulb will not glow (1)

13 a) cheese contains protein and fat, butter contains fat, bread contains starch   b) orange

14 a) magnesium sulphate + copper   b) copper

15 when the bell push is pressed the circuit is made complete and the electromagnet is turned on (1), the soft iron armature is pulled towards the electromagnet and the hammer hits the gong (1), a gap is created at the contact screw and the electromagnet is turned off (1), the armature springs back to its original position and the whole process starts again (1)

16 a) the synovial fluid reduces friction/prevents the bones sliding and grinding against each other and causing damage

b) cartilage acts as a shock absorber/protects the bones from knocking together and wearing away.

17 a) stoma – where carbon dioxide enters the leaf / waxy layer – prevents the leaf from losing too much water palisade layer – the place where most photosynthesis takes place / leaf vein – transports water and minerals to the leaf

b) chlorophyll and sunlight